HANDBOOK

NUMBER EIGHT

# A Mathematical Olympiad Companion

Geoff Smith

The United Kingdom Mathematics Trust

A Mathematical Olympiad Companion



Published by The United Kingdom Mathematics Trust.
Maths Challenges Office, School of Mathematics, University of Leeds,
Leeds, LS2 9JT, United Kingdom
http://www.ukmt.org.uk

First published 2016.

ISBN 978-1-906001-28-5

Printed in the UK for the UKMT by The Charlesworth Group, Wakefield.
http://www.charlesworth.com

Typographic design by Andrew Jobbings of Arbelos.
http://www.arbelos.co.uk

Typeset with LaTeX.

The books published by the United Kingdom Mathematics Trust are grouped into series.

The EXCURSIONS IN MATHEMATICS series consists of monographs which focus on a particular topic of interest and investigate it in some detail, using a wide range of ideas and techniques. They are aimed at high school students, undergraduates and others who are prepared to pursue a subject in some depth, but do not require specialised knowledge.

1. *The Backbone of Pascal's Triangle*, Martin Griffiths
2. *A Prime Puzzle*, Martin Griffiths

The HANDBOOKS series is aimed particularly at students at secondary school who are interested in acquiring the knowledge and skills which are useful for tackling challenging problems, such as those posed in the competitions administered by the UKMT and similar organisations.

1. *Plane Euclidean Geometry: Theory and Problems*, A D Gardiner and C J Bradley
2. *Introduction to Inequalities*, C J Bradley
3. *A Mathematical Olympiad Primer*, Geoff C Smith
4. *Introduction to Number Theory*, C J Bradley
5. *A Problem Solver's Handbook*, Andrew Jobbings
6. *Introduction to Combinatorics*, Gerry Leversha and Dominic Rowland
7. *First Steps for Problem Solvers*, Mary Teresa Fyfe and Andrew Jobbings
8. *A Mathematical Olympiad Companion*, Geoff C Smith

The PATHWAYS series aims to provide classroom teaching material for use in secondary schools. Each title develops a subject in more depth and in more detail than is normally required by public examinations or national curricula.

1. *Crossing the Bridge*, Gerry Leversha
2. *The Geometry of the Triangle*, Gerry Leversha

The PROBLEMS series consists of collections of high-quality and original problems of Olympiad standard.

1. *New Problems in Euclidean Geometry*, David Monk

❖

The CHALLENGES series is aimed at students at secondary school who are interested in tackling stimulating problems, such as those posed in the Mathematical Challenges administered by the UKMT and similar organisations.

1. *Ten Years of Mathematical Challenges: 1997 to 2006*
2. *Ten Further Years of Mathematical Challenges: 2006 to 2016*
3. *Intermediate Problems*, Andrew Jobbings
4. *Junior Problems*, Andrew Jobbings

The YEARBOOKS series documents all the UKMT activities, including details of all the challenge papers and solutions, lists of high scorers, accounts of the IMO and Olympiad training camps, and other information about the Trust's work during each year.

# Contents

# Series Editor's Foreword

This book is part of a series whose aim is to help young mathematicians prepare for competitions, such as the British Mathematical Olympiad, at secondary school level. Like previous volumes in the Handbooks series, this book provides cheap and ready access to directly relevant material. All these books are characterized by the large number of carefully constructed exercises for the reader to attempt.

I hope that every secondary school will have these books in its library. The prices have been set so low that many good students will wish to purchase their own copies. Schools wishing to give out large numbers of copies of these books as prizes should note that discounts may be negotiated with the UKMT office.

London, UK GERRY LEVERSHA

## About the author

Geoff Smith is a Senior Lecturer in Mathematics at the University of Bath. He has been involved in mathematics enrichment since 1991 when he helped to found the *Royal Institution Mathematics Masterclasses* in Bath and Bristol (and later in Swindon). He was UK IMO team leader for all years since 2002 with two exceptions, and has led national teams to both the Balkan Mathematical Olympiad and the Romanian Masters of Mathematics. He was appointed chair of the British Mathematical Olympiad Subtrust in 2006. In 2010 the IMO jury elected him to serve on its council, the IMO Advisory Board, for 2010–2014, and they elected him Chair of the IMO Advisory Board to serve 2014–18.

He edited the first two of UKMT's series of books, *Plane Euclidean Geometry* and *Introductions to Number Theory and Inequalities.* He has written two texts for Springer:– *Introduction to University Mathematics: Algebra and Analysis* is to help students make the transition to university mathematics, and *Topics in Group Theory*, written with Olga Tabachnikova, is for a more advanced audience.

He has had 10 successful PhD students, and does research in group theory and lately also classical and projective geometry. He works out of his main areas from time to time, and so also has research publications in computer op-code design, DNA sequencing and snail venom.

Geoff Smith was awarded an MBE in the 2011 Birthday Honours for his services to education.

He is married with two children and lives in Bath.

# Preface

## Acknowledgements

I thank the problem setters, the problem selection committee, the students who participate, and their teachers who provide them with coaching and encouragement.

I also express my gratitude to the markers who gather to assess the scripts with quiet efficiency, the small heroic team who put together the solutions booklet in short order and the UKMT volunteers and employees who make all this possible.

In addition I am grateful to the editorial team comprising James Gazet, Andrew Jobbings, Gerry Leversha and Nick Lord for eliminating many infelicities and for creating excellent diagrams.

I also thank Mr Michael Ng of Aylesbury Grammar School for his assiduous work when reading a draft version of this text.

Bath, UK　　　　Geoff Smith

# Chapter 1

# Introduction

This book is a compendium of problems which have been set in the second round of the British Mathematical Olympiad in the years 2002–16.

There are three additional problems in this book which were used in a fictional mathematical olympiad, staged as part of a feature film called *X plus Y* in many countries and *A Brilliant Young Mind* in the USA. It has various other titles in dubbed versions.

Every year, BMO publishes a solutions pamphlet after the competition, with the solutions mostly inspired by the candidates' scripts. These booklets are distributed both nationally and to leaders and deputies at the International Mathematical Olympiad in July. Later, a version of these solutions appears in the annual Yearbook of the United Kingdom Mathematics Trust. Until 2001, both rounds of BMO happened in the same calendar year, but then the schedule was changed to have round 1 before Christmas, and round 2 early in the new year.

When the word "olympiad" forms part of the title of a competition such as the British Mathematical Olympiad, we put it in capital letters. We use lower case when alluding generally to mathematics olympiads for secondary school students at national or international level.

## 1.1 How should you use this book?

Well, you can use it how you wish, as a doorstop or as material for lining the floor of a hamster cage. If you wish to strengthen your skills as a mathematical olympiad competitor, then the method I recommend is to tackle the problems one by one, at first paying no attention to the solutions section. Reading olympiad problems and their solutions like a novel is a really bad idea. You only get significant benefit from looking at a solution if you have tried to solve the problem yourself, so looking at the solution immediately is a waste of a problem.

Can you solve a special case? Can you solve an easier version of the problem, one with small numbers in it? Play with the problem. Look at it from many different points of view.

So, how long should you spend on a problem before you resort to looking up a solution? Well, that is a matter for the reader. It depends on your willingness to persevere. If you are very determined to solve a problem unaided, you are likely to become stronger and stronger the more time you spend thinking about mathematics. That does not answer the question of course. I suggest that you should not consider yourself to have engaged with a problem unless you have thought about it (and nothing else) for at least a couple of hours. If you are prepared to set the threshold higher, at 5 or 10 hours, so much the better. If and when you become a research mathematician, you will think it perfectly normal to ponder on a problem for months or years.

The students sitting BMO2 have 3 hours 30 minutes to address the four problems. Many students fail to solve any problems, and only very good candidates get two questions right. It is rare for a student to answer all four problems correctly. The problems are intended to be on a gradient, with Problem 1 being relatively accessible and Problem 4 being much harder. The setters sometimes make errors of judgement about this, so you have no guarantee that your assessment of the relative difficulty of the problems will coincide with that of the setting committee. The moral is: do not ignore Problem 4. You might have just the right set of ideas to dispose of it quickly.

## 1.2 How should I write things up?

It is important to become skilled at writing up your solutions well, so as to maximize the credit that your script will attract and to minimize the time you spend worrying about issues of presentation.

* Write on plain A4 paper (or the size *Letter* in some countries). Plain paper scans and photocopies better than lined paper, and is the best background for diagrams.

- Distinguish between rough pages and polished well-written solutions.
- Written-up solutions should be in ink.
- Use just one side of the paper in case it needs to be scanned or photocopied.
- Do not mix work on different problems on the same page. This minimizes the danger of work being overlooked.
- Draw each diagram in pencil and on a dedicated separate page. This enables you, and the marker, to refer to the diagram while reading a solution which may be on many sides of paper. Draw (in pencil) the best diagram that time allows. If the diagram will be scanned or photocopied, make sure that the lines are not faint.
- Marks may be given to work written in rough. Therefore note down all your ideas, even if you do not follow up on them.
- Correct and precise language becomes a habit of mind, and helps with problem solving.
- State what you are going to prove, and then do it.
- Do not waste time proving standard results.
- It is often easiest if you break up your argument into parts, and give proofs for the various sections separately. Explain how the parts fit together.
- If you are giving a solution to an "if, and only if" problem, it is usually best to regard this as two separate tasks. State which of the implications you are proving each time.
- If you are doing an induction argument, make it clear what the statement is that you are trying to prove, and give the name of the quantity which will be involved in the induction. Write 'base case' and check that this case holds. Then write 'inductive step' and give the appropriate argument. Finish with "by induction, the result is proved".
- If you are giving an argument by contradiction, clearly announce what you are doing.
- Your proofs should be decorated with English sentences and explanatory asides. Please label statements and equations to which you need to refer (and no others).

- In combinatorics, there is a sin called "pattern spotting" which occurs when the student sees a pattern emerging by looking at small examples, and then simply asserts that the observed pattern always holds. This has the status of a conjecture (that is, an informed guess), and is a valuable part of the process of understanding what might be going on. However, it is not a mathematical proof of anything, and so is unlikely to attract many marks.
- From the markers' point of view, the most difficult scripts are essays, where the overall structure of the proof is somewhere between clear and unclear. Short explicit statements giving signposts to the marker are very helpful.
- Reasoning needs to be explained. A list of correct equations with no commentary is of limited value. This is particularly true in geometry problems.
- Your work does not have to be formal, but it does have to be clear.
- Distinguish between a theorem and its converse. Be careful because not all converses are true.
- If you have poor handwriting, then improve it. As an interim measure, if your hand does not distinguish between $m$ and $n$, or between $u$ and $v$, then avoid these letters whenever possible.

Think of the marker as an old friend who is slightly pedantic but well meaning. You need to explain things to them very clearly, because the poor thing is not good at filling in the gaps in an explanation. It also helps to regard the marker as being slightly myopic, and having lost their glasses. They appreciate good handwriting and short, clear sentences.

## 1.3 Should my solutions be the same as the ones in the book?

In a word, no.

Some problems have a natural method of solution, and under real examination conditions, everyone who solves the problem uses the same method. However there are lots of problems where there are multiple methods of solution, and in this book we have not attempted an exhaustive description of possible solutions.

The situation regarding geometry problems is that they all seem to admit very many solutions. This is not just because of the range of techniques which can be deployed to address plane geometry problems, including classical Euclidean methods, geometric transformations (similarities), vectors, reflection methods, Cartesian coordinates, trigonometry, complex numbers, areal and trilinear coordinates, projective geometry, inversive geometry, tiling, embedding the problem in three dimensions, regarding the configuration as a mechanical system and origami. No, it is not just the multiplicity of methods, it is also the diversity of the ways in which these methods can be used. People also mix methods, using different techniques to do different parts of the problem.

Another important thing to remember is that solutions given in books are highly polished, unlike a script submitted in a mathematics competition. As soon as a student has written up a correct solution to a problem, they move on, and ignore that question until the exam is over. On the other hand, people who write books try to polish the mathematics to make it readily understandable and also to look stylish and elegant. Some succeed better than others of course.

## 1.4 What do I need to know?

MOST MATHEMATICAL OLYMPIAD PROBLEMS CAN BE SOLVED WITHOUT THE USE OF ADVANCED THEOREMS.

Indeed, the problem setters try to design the exam papers to have that property. However, it is often handy to know some theory, and if you do that, then you may find that you can write down solutions more easily. It is also the case that the act of learning some theorems, and their proofs, gives you a more confident understanding of the mathematical geography, so that during a mathematics competition, you may find yourself thinking "I have seen something a bit like this before". That is a very comforting thought.

The area where theory can most readily be applied to give novel solutions is geometry. Do not worry if you were not previously familiar with a piece of theory given in a solution that you read in this book or elsewhere. It is always possible to avoid citing geometry theorems, even if that means reinventing the results yourself.

## 1.5 How does marking work?

There are two marking schemes for each problem. One is for scripts which answer the problem correctly, possibly with minor imperfections, and another for scripts where the problem is not solved.

At the International Mathematical Olympiad the score for a perfect answer to a question is 7. Very few scripts obtain 4 marks, and the most common marks for a problem are 0, 1, 2, 6 and 7. The mark scheme will reward full solutions far more than scripts where partial progress is made. An incomplete proof is not a proof, and so is not worth many marks. There are no marks awarded for style, and any logically correct argument will do as an answer. At the IMO there are special prizes for exceptionally beautiful solutions or generalizations, but in recent years these prizes have been awarded very sparingly, the most recent being to Iurie Boreico of Moldova in 2005.

National mathematical olympiads have their own marking regimes, and in the British Mathematical Olympiad, each problem is marked out of 10, so the most common scores for a problem are 0, 1, 2, 8, 9 and 10.

## 1.6 Directed angles

Many geometric configurations, when described in words, can give rise to different diagrams depending on arbitrary choices made by the person doing the drawing. If a triangle is obtuse (so it involves an angle bigger than 90°), then the circumcentre and orthocentre of the triangle will be strictly outside the triangle. If the triangle is acute-angled, these points will be inside the triangle (and both points will be on the triangle itself if there is a right angle in play). This is just one example, and there are endless other circumstances where multiple configurations can arise.

Do not worry about this too much. Sometimes marking schemes impose a small fine for not dealing with multiple configurations, but often they do not. If you solve your geometry problems using algebra (including trigonometry), then this issue sometimes disappears because the diagram is redundant. People who like to use classical Euclidean methods have developed a defence against this problem. They often work with directed angles and signed angles (which are not necessarily the same thing!). There are various conventions as to how to set this up in a consistent way. I recommend the formalism developed in pages 3–13 of [4], available for free download from the internet. The conventions are crystallized on page 12 of that book.

Be aware that there are other formalisms, and do not assume that someone using angle conventions is necessarily following Kedlaya's procedure. For example, Gerry Leversha does not use Kedlaya's conventions in his UKMT texts.

If you use a good system of conventions, then some theorems will become unified. For example: angles subtended by an arc of a circle are equal (angles in the same segment) is the same result, with the same proof, as the fact that an exterior angle of a cyclic quadrilateral is equal to the interior opposite angle. You can take the proof, and draw an illustration. The diagram you produce will depend on the particular cyclic order of four labelled points.

I am not proposing to use this book as propaganda for this technique, but it seems sensible at least to try to give geometric descriptions in a consistent way. For the purposes of this book triangles and other polygons are, by default, anticlockwise objects. There are area formulas for triangles which yield minus the correct answer when the vertices are specified in clockwise order. Therefore it makes sense to view area as a signed quantity. It is also helpful to use consistent angle descriptions. Come in along a line, and turn left, so in triangle $ABC$ the internal angle at $B$ is $\angle ABC$, and definitely not $\angle CBA$ which denotes the reflex angle.

This policy has not always been applied in the past, and so when you look at old BMO problems, you sometimes find reckless descriptions of angles, with no heed paid to the demands of consistency. I have kept the original wording of the problems in this book. Of course, you are sometimes forced to consider clockwise triangles, particularly in the context of indirect similarity.

## 1.7 Further reading

There are excellent books for olympiad mathematicians in languages other than English. In the United Kingdom, the publications arm of the UK Mathematics Trust publishes many books which I can recommend unreservedly. Please purchase such books directly from the Trust's website `www.ukmt.org.uk` (and do not leave off the "uk") or from a major internet bookshop.

It may well be that you have already read my text *A Mathematical Olympiad Primer* [9], which is aimed at students sitting their first mathematical olympiad exam. The book in your hands is a more advanced version of [9]. The UKMT books for students who are likely readers of *A Mathematical Olympiad Companion* are [1, 2, 3, 5, 6, 7, 8]. No doubt more texts will appear over time. These books are available direct from UKMT and also via a major internet bookseller.

# Chapter 2

# Facts and terminology

At first reading, perhaps it would be best to skip this chapter and proceed with trying to solve problems. You can refer back to this chapter as necessary and as light relief. We will briefly address the following topics.

- The theory of inequalities.
- The power of a point theorem in plane geometry.
- The nine-point circle.
- Isogonal conjugacy.
- Induction.
- Factorization of integers.
- The Chinese remainder theorem.

This is a short explanation of some facts and items of terminology which will appear in some of the solutions. There is much more theory here than you will need to solve the problems in this text. However, we are mindful of international readers whose national maths olympiads may rely on more theory than is usual in the United Kingdom. It is also the case that some British readers will harbour the ambition to participate in international mathematics competitions, and such people will wish to be well prepared.

In this preliminary chapter, we will summarize results from several areas which may well be beyond the normal secondary school syllabus in some countries, but nonetheless are sometimes useful in national mathematical olympiads and international mathematics competitions.

## 2.1 Inequalities

The most basic inequality is that sums of squares are positive or zero. Some well-known inequalities depend on the quantities involved being non-negative, and others do not. Since it is important to remember which is which, we make two lists.

This brief summary of celebrated inequalities is little more than an *aide memoire*, and we refer the interested reader to [1].

The list of inequalities here is perhaps a little more comprehensive than it needs to be. The basic inequalities are: sums of squares are non-negative, the triangle inequality, AM-GM, Rearrangement and Cauchy-Schwarz. The HM-GM-AM-RMS chain probably comes next. Then look at power means, Jensen's inequality and Hölder's inequality. Finally, international competitors need to keep a grip on Muirhead and Schur's inequalities, otherwise three-variable symmetric inequalities will start to appear in mathematics competitions again, as welcome as *Calystegia sepium* in your garden.

### No sign restriction on quantities

**The triangle inequality** *The route of shortest distance between two points is a straight line segment.*

It follows that in a non-degenerate triangle, each side is shorter than the sum of the lengths of the other two sides. Referring to the triangle in figure 2.1, we have $AB < BC + CA$, with similar results for the other two sides.

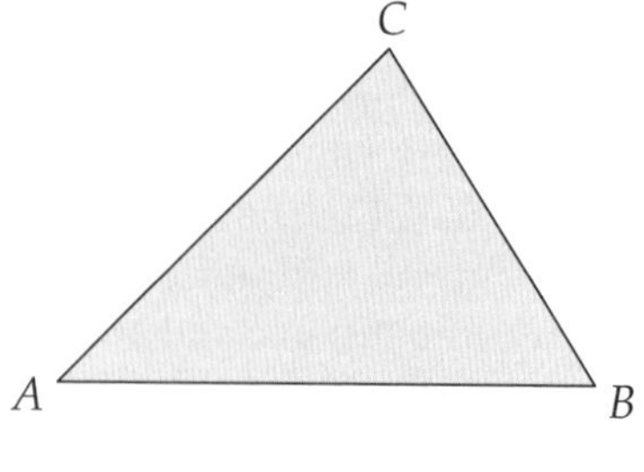


*Figure 2.1*

This apparently innocent observation has many consequences.

Oddly enough, it is very common to consider what happens when the triangle is degenerate (that is, flat). In this situation we may assume that the vertices are points on the real line at $p_1, p_2$ and $p_3$. It is important that we are not assuming that they occur in that order. See the example shown in figure 2.2.

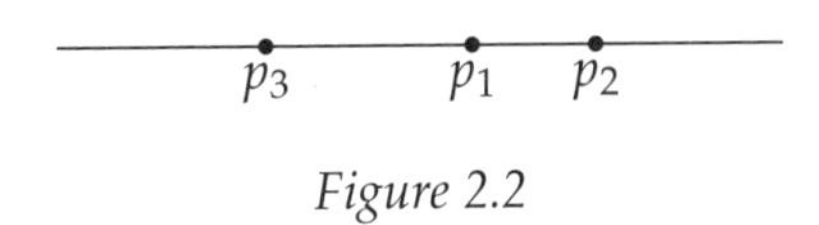


*Figure 2.2*

Let $x_1 = p_2 - p_1$ and $x_2 = p_3 - p_2$ so $x_1 + x_2 = p_3 - p_1$. The triangle inequality then asserts that

$$|x_1 + x_2| \leq |x_1| + |x_2| \tag{2.1}$$

for all real numbers $x_1$ and $x_2$. Notice that it follows by induction that for all real numbers $x_1, x_2, \ldots, x_n$, we have

$$|x_1 + x_2 + \cdots + x_n| \leq |x_1| + |x_2| + \cdots + |x_n|$$

which we might call the generalized triangle inequality.

Put $y_1 = x_1$ and $y_2 = x_1 + x_2$ in the triangle inequality (2.1) to obtain

$$|y_2| \leq |y_1| + |y_2 - y_1|$$

or equivalently

$$|y_2| - |y_1| \leq |y_1 - y_2|$$

for all real numbers $y_1$ and $y_2$. Exchanging the roles of $y_1$ and $y_2$ we obtain

$$|y_1| - |y_2| \leq |y_1 - y_2|.$$

One of the last two inequalities (but we do not know which) asserts that

$$\Big| |y_1| - |y_2| \Big| \leq |y_1 - y_2|$$

for all real numbers $y_1$ and $y_2$. This is known as the *reversed* triangle inequality.

These inequalities are exceptionally important. They should become very familiar to you, so that they spring from your pen with the least encouragement. To begin the process of familiarization, please determine when these inequalities become equalities.

**The Cauchy-Schwarz inequality** *Suppose that $x_1, x_2, \ldots, x_n$ and $y_1, y_2, \ldots, y_n$ are two lists of real numbers, then*

$$x_1y_1 + x_2y_2 + \cdots + x_ny_n \leq \sqrt{x_1^2 + x_2^2 + \cdots + x_n^2} \times \sqrt{y_1^2 + y_2^2 + \cdots + y_n^2}$$

*or if you prefer*

$$(x_1y_1 + x_2y_2 + \cdots + x_ny_n)^2 \leq (x_1^2 + x_2^2 + \cdots + x_n^2)(y_1^2 + y_2^2 + \cdots + y_n^2).$$

This has a geometric interpretation if you are working in the plane or in three-dimensional space using identically calibrated axes at right angles. The dot or scalar product of two vectors is the product of their lengths multiplied by the cosine of the angle between them. The Cauchy-Schwarz inequality can be interpreted as saying that the values of cosine are trapped between $-1$ and 1.

In some cultures the Ukrainian mathematician Bunyakovsky is given at least partial credit for this inequality, on the ground that he discovered it second, and so has a better claim than Schwarz.

The next result generalizes the Cauchy-Schwarz inequality. Hölder's inequality becomes Cauchy-Schwarz when $p = q = 2$.

**Hölder's inequality** *Suppose that $x_1, x_2, \ldots, x_n$ and $y_1, y_2, \ldots, y_n$ are two lists of real numbers and that $\frac{1}{p} + \frac{1}{q} = 1$ where $p, q > 1$, then*

$$|x_1y_1| + |x_2y_2| + \cdots + |x_ny_n| \leq (|x_1|^p + |x_2|^p + \cdots + |x_n|^p)^{\frac{1}{p}} (|y_1|^q + |y_2|^q + \cdots + |y_n|^q)^{\frac{1}{q}}.$$

Now suppose that $x_1, x_2, \ldots, x_n$ and $y_1, y_2, \ldots, y_n$ are two lists of real numbers both arranged in weakly increasing order. We use the word *weakly* because the inequalities are not strict. Therefore $x_1 \leq x_2 \leq \cdots \leq x_n$ and $y_1 \leq y_2 \leq \cdots \leq y_n$. The game is to pair the members off in some way, and then consider the size of the sum of the products:

$$s_\pi = x_1y_{\pi(1)} + x_2y_{\pi(2)} + \cdots + x_ny_{\pi(n)}.$$

Here $\pi$ is a permutation of $1, 2, \ldots, n$. For example, if $n = 2$ and $\pi$ is the identity permutation id, then

$$s_{id} = x_1y_1 + x_2y_2.$$

However, if $\tau$ is the non-identity permutation which swaps 1 and 2, then

$$s_\tau = x_1y_2 + x_2y_1.$$

If $n = 3$ there are 6 possible permutations, and in general there are $n!$ permutations. The problem is to determine which permutations will maximize and minimize the expression.

**The rearrangement inequality** *The expression is maximized by using the identity permutation. The largest possible expression is*

$$x_1y_1 + x_2y_2 + \cdots + x_ny_n.$$

*The expression is minimised using the permutation which reverses the list. The smallest possible expression is*

$$x_1y_n + x_2y_{n-1} + \cdots + x_ny_1.$$

For example, if the first list is $-3$, $-1$, 1, 10 and the second is $-10$, 1, $\sqrt{3}$, 2 then the maximum expression is

$$30 - 1 + \sqrt{3} + 20 = 49 + \sqrt{3}$$

and the minimum expression is

$$-6 - \sqrt{3} + 1 - 100 = -105 - \sqrt{3}.$$

There are 22 other possible expressions, the values of which are trapped between these two bounds.

**Chebyshev's inequality** *Suppose that $x_1 \le x_2 \le \cdots \le x_n$ and $y_1 \le y_2 \le \cdots \le y_n$ are weakly increasing lists of real numbers. Then*

$$\frac{x_1y_n + x_2y_{n-1} + \cdots + x_ny_1}{n} \le \left(\frac{x_1 + x_2 + \cdots + x_n}{n}\right)\left(\frac{y_1 + y_2 + \cdots + y_n}{n}\right) \le \frac{x_1y_1 + x_2y_2 + \cdots + x_ny_n}{n}.$$

A *convex subset* $S$ of the plane is a set with the property that if $A$ and $B$ are in $S$, then every point on the line segment joining $A$ to $B$ is in $S$. A function $f$ defined on an interval is said to be *convex* if the region of the plane above the graph of $f$ is convex. An *interval* is a connected subset of the real line, so the set $\mathbb{R}$ of real numbers, $\{r \mid r \in \mathbb{R},\ -1 < r \leq 100\}$ and the empty set are all intervals. The sets

$$\{x \mid 1 \leq x \leq 10\} \cup \{y \mid -10 < y - 3\} \text{ and } \{z \mid z \in \mathbb{R},\ z \neq \pi\}$$

are not intervals, though each is the union of two intervals.

Thus the functions defined by each of the following formulas is convex: $x^2$, $e^x$ defined on the whole real line; $x^3$, -$\log x$ for $x > 0$; $-\cos x$ and $\tan x$ for $0 < x < \frac{1}{2}\pi$.

**Jensen's inequality** *If the function $f$ is convex, then*

$$f\left(\frac{x_1 + x_2 + \cdots + x_n}{n}\right) \leq \frac{f(x_1) + f(x_2) + \cdots + f(x_n)}{n}.$$

Informally, the reason this inequality is valid is that the $n$ points $(x_i, f(x_i))$ are on the graph of the function. Their average position (centre of mass) is not below the graph by convexity considerations, and that statement translates to Jensen's inequality.

There is a concave version. A function is concave if the region below the graph is convex. Think of the mouth of a cave. Examples include $\log x$ when $x > 0$ and $\cos x$ for $-\frac{1}{2}\pi \leq x \leq \frac{1}{2}\pi$. In this version of Jensen's inequality, we have

$$f\left(\frac{x_1 + x_2 + \cdots + x_n}{n}\right) \geq \frac{f(x_1) + f(x_2) + \cdots + f(x_n)}{n}.$$

Either version implies the other, by replacing $f$ by $-f$.

## Quantities are non-negative

**AM-GM inequality** *Suppose that $x_1, x_2, \ldots, x_n$ are non-negative real numbers, then*

$$\sqrt[n]{x_1 x_2 \cdots x_n} \leq \frac{x_1 + x_2 + \cdots + x_n}{n}.$$

The left expression is the *geometric mean* and the right one is the *arithmetic mean* (the common or garden average).

**HM-GM inequality** *Suppose that $x_1, x_2, \ldots, x_n$ are positive. Then*

$$\frac{n}{x_1^{-1} + x_2^{-1} + \cdots + x_n^{-1}} \leq \sqrt[n]{x_1 x_2 \cdots x_n}.$$

The expression on the left is the *harmonic mean* of the numbers—the inverse of the mean of their inverses.

**AM-QM inequality (or AM-RMS inequality)**

$$\frac{x_1 + x_2 + \cdots + x_n}{n} \leq \sqrt{\frac{x_1^2 + x_2^2 + \cdots + x_n^2}{n}}.$$

The expression on the right is the *quadratic mean* or *root mean square*.

Let $p$ be a non-zero real number and suppose that $x_1, x_2, \ldots, x_n \geq 0$. The *power mean* associated with $p$ is

$$M_p = \left( \frac{x_1^p + x_2^p + \cdots + x_n^p}{n} \right)^{\frac{1}{p}}.$$

Although we have barred $p = 0$, the limit of $M_p$ as $p$ approaches 0 turns out to be the geometric mean of these quantities. We therefore define $M_0$ to be the geometric mean.

**The power mean inequality** *If $p < q$, then $M_p \leq M_q$.*

Notice that $M_{-1}$ is the harmonic mean, $M_0$ the geometric mean, $M_1$ the arithmetic mean and $M_2$ is the root mean square. Therefore the power mean inequality gives us:

$$\text{HM} \leq \text{GM} \leq \text{AM} \leq \text{RMS}. \tag{2.2}$$

## Muirhead's and Schur's inequalities

These inequalities are very useful for solving problems about symmetric sums of non-negative quantities. This is technical material and should be understood by students competing at international level.

## 2.2 Power of a point

Many readers will be familiar with two theorems concerning lines that intersect a circle.

The first of these is the *intersecting chords theorem*. This is illustrated in figure 2.3 which shows two chords $AB$ and $CD$ intersecting at a point $P$ inside a circle.

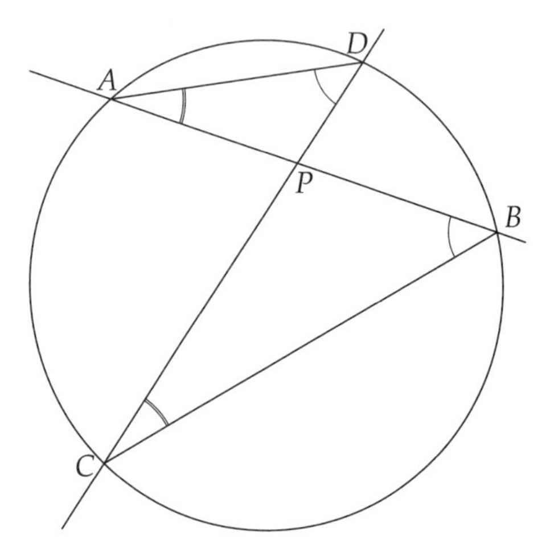


*Figure 2.3*

By two applications of angle in the same segment, (clockwise) triangle $PAD$ is similar to triangle $PCB$, and hence

$$\frac{PA}{PC} = \frac{PD}{PB}$$

and multiplying out we obtain

$$PA \times PB = PC \times PD.$$

The second result, which is closely related, is the *tangent-secant theorem*. A secant is a line which meets a circle twice, whereas a tangent is a line which meets it at a single point. Suppose that $P$ is a point outside a circle. Draw two secant lines, $PAB$ and $PCD$ as shown in figure 2.4.

We allow the possibility that one of these lines is a tangent, so we draw the line $PT$ to illustrate this possibility. Once again it follows that triangles

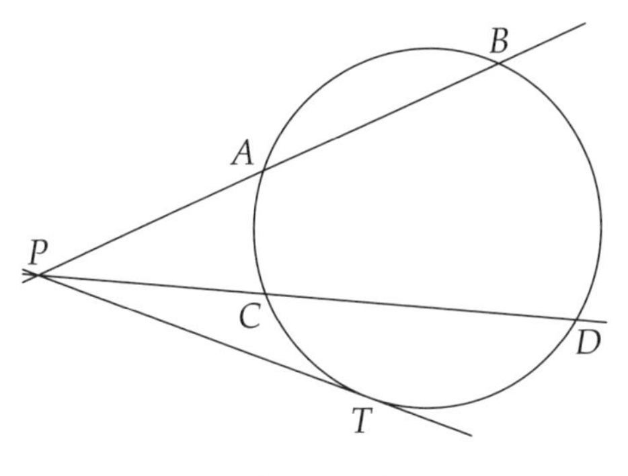


*Figure 2.4*

$PAD$ and $PCD$ are (indirectly) similar triangles. Once again it follows that

$$PA \times PB = PC \times PD.$$

Also $PAT$ is (indirectly) similar to $PTB$, using the alternate segment theorem, so

$$PA \times PB = PT^2.$$

This is precisely what is obtained by putting $A = B = T$ in the secant version of the result.

These three results about tangents, secants and chords are unified by the idea that the quantity $PA \times PB$ depends on the relative positions of the point $P$ and the circle, but does not depend on which chord, secant or tangent is used to define $A$ and $B$.

Prompted by this, we refer to $PA \times PB$ as the *power of P* with respect to the circle. It is helpful to make this a signed quantity. This can be done by assigning an arbitrary direction to the line through $P$, and then regarding $PA$ and $PB$ as directed (that is, signed) lengths. Thus if $P$ is outside the circle, it will have positive power, but if $P$ is inside the circle, $PA$ and $PB$ are in opposite directions so the power of $P$ is negative. The power of a point $P$ on the circle is 0.

Let the circle have centre $O$ and radius $R$. If $P$ is outside the circle, the power of $P$ is $PT^2$ (figure 2.4) and by the theorem of Pythagoras, this is $OP^2 - R^2$. Exactly the same formula is valid for $P$ inside the circle. See figure 2.5.

If you are familiar with vector notation, then a neat way to define the power of $P$ with respect to the circle is to have a line through $P$ which

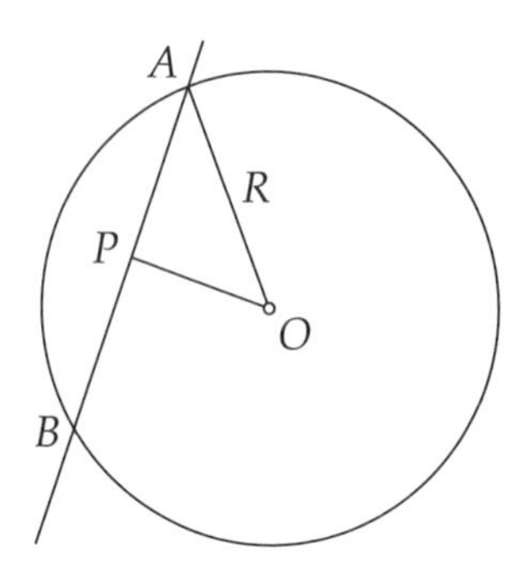


*Figure 2.5*

meets the circle at $A$ and $B$. Then define the power of $P$ with respect to the circle to be the dot (scalar) product of vectors: $\boldsymbol{PA}.\boldsymbol{PB}$. This quantity is positive when both vectors are pointing the same way, so when $P$ is outside the circle. It is negative if the vectors are pointing in opposite directions, which happens when $P$ is inside the circle. It is 0 if $P$ is on the circle.

Many readers will be familiar with the Cartesian equation of a circle with centre $O = (a, b)$ and radius $r$. The equation is

$$(x-a)^2 + (y-b)^2 - r^2 = 0$$

or equally well

$$x^2 + y^2 - 2ax - 2by + a^2 + b^2 - r^2 = 0.$$

The power of a point $P = (x, y)$ with respect to the circle defined by this equation is $PO^2 - r^2$ is $(x-a)^2 + (y-b)^2 - r^2$ or equivalently $x^2 + y^2 - 2ax - 2by + a^2 + b^2 - r^2$. The locus of points $P$ such that the power of $P$ with respect to a particular circle with centre $O$ is constant is also a circle with centre $O$.

Now suppose that you have circles $\Sigma_1$ and $\Sigma_2$ with different centres $(a_1, b_1)$ and $(a_2, b_2)$, and radii $r_1$ and $r_2$. The powers of $P$ with respect to these circles will be equal precisely when

$$(x-a_1)^2 + (y-b_1)^2 - r_1^2 = (x-a_2)^2 + (y-b_2)^2 - r_2^2$$

which can be rewritten as

$$2(a_1 - a_2)x + 2(b_1 - b_2)y + k = 0,$$

where $k$ is a constant. This is the equation of a line called the *radical axis* of the two circles. If two circles intersect, then their radical axis is the straight line through their points of intersection. If two circles are tangent (internally or externally), then their radical axis is the line tangent to both circles at their point of tangency.

The radical axis of a pair of circles is symmetric with respect to reflection in the line of centres, so the radical axis is either perpendicular to the line of centres or it is the line of centres. Clearly it is not the latter, so the radical axis is perpendicular to the line of centres.

If three circles have different centres on a line, then the three radical axes of the circles (taken in pairs) are parallel since they are all perpendicular to the common lines of centres. If the three circles have centres which are not collinear, then the three radical axes meet at the *radical centre* of the three circles, the unique point which has the same power with respect to each of the three circles. See figure 2.6.

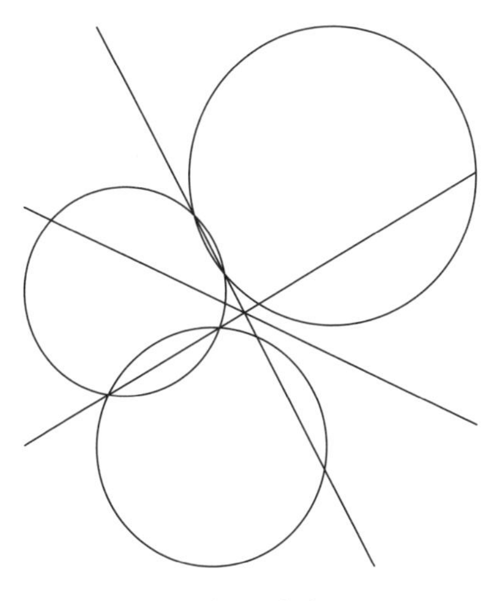

*Figure 2.6*

## 2.3 The nine-point circle

We refer the reader to a good book on Euclidean geometry, such as [6], for a more detailed explanation of the Euler line and the nine-point circle. See figure 2.7 on the next page.

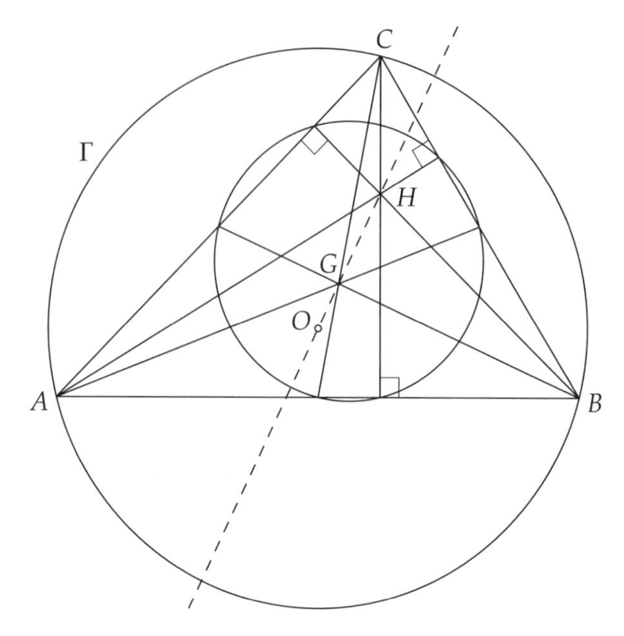


*Figure 2.7*

Suppose that $ABC$ is a triangle. The circumcircle $\Gamma$ of this triangle has centre $O$ which is the point where the perpendicular bisectors of the three sides meet. The median lines of triangle $ABC$ meet at the centroid $G$ of triangle $ABC$. The altitudes of triangle $ABC$ meet at the orthocentre $H$ of triangle $ABC$. The three points $OGH$ are collinear on the Euler line, and $G$ is always between $O$ and $H$. In fact $OG : GH = 1 : 2$.

Enlarge $\Gamma$ from $H$ with scale factor $\frac{1}{2}$, and also enlarge $\Gamma$ from $G$ with scale factor $-\frac{1}{2}$. Each of these two enlargements carries $O$ to the midpoint of $OH$, and each carries $\Gamma$ to a circle of half its radius. Therefore these two circles are the same. The fact that this new circle has a dual identity enables you to read off nine important points which lie on this circle: the feet of the altitudes of ABC, the midpoints of the sides of triangle $ABC$ and the midpoints of the three line segments joining $H$ to the vertices of triangle $ABC$. This circle is called the *nine-point circle*, or sometimes the *Feuerbach circle*.

## 2.4 Isogonal conjugacy

Suppose that $ABC$ is a triangle and that $P$ is a point in the plane which does not lie on a side line of $ABC$. The line $AP$ can be reflected in the internal or external angle bisector at $A$ to give the same line. The lines $BP$ and $CP$ can be given similar treatment by cyclic change of letters. If $P$ lies on the circumcircle of $ABC$, then these three newly minted lines are parallel. Otherwise these three new lines meet at a point $P'$ called the *isogonal conjugate* of $P$.

Note that the distribution of angles in the corners of the diagram (see figure 2.8) ensures that $P$ is the isogonal conjugate of $P'$.

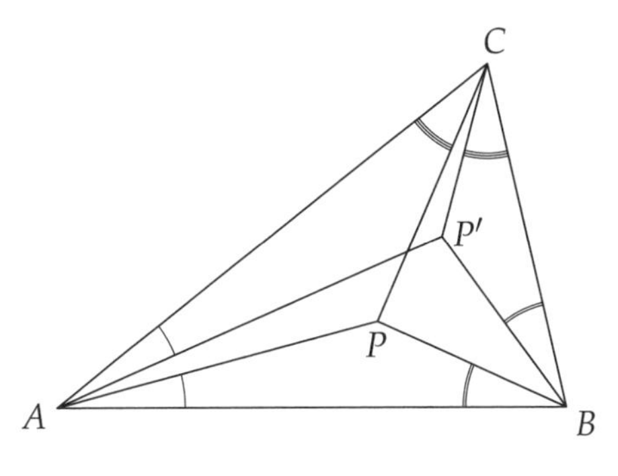


*Figure 2.8*

The incentre of $ABC$ and the three excentres of $ABC$ are each their own isogonal conjugate. The circumcentre and orthocentre are isogonal conjugates unless $ABC$ involves a right angle. This can be proved by using a simple angle chase. The isogonal conjugate of the centroid $G$ of a triangle is the symmedian point (also known as the Grebe or Lemoine point), a point of great significance in the projective geometry of the triangle.

## 2.5 Induction

### Ordinary induction

Suppose that $P(n)$ is a statement about the positive integer $n$. $P(n)$ might be the statement that the sum of the first $n$ odd positive integers is a square (but it might not). Naturally you will look at a few examples to see what is going on, you will quickly be persuaded that the result may well be true.

A proof by mathematical induction, in its simplest form, has the following shape:

**Base case**

Check that $P(1)$ is true.

**Inductive step**

Show that, for each positive integer $r$, if $P(r)$ is true, then it follows that $P(r+1)$ is true.

If you can do both of those things, then you are allowed to conclude that $P(n)$ is true for every positive integer $n$. The reason that this is valid as that $P(1)$ is true because you checked the base case. Now the inductive step applies when $r = 1$, thus $P(2)$ is true. Now the inductive step applies when $r = 2$, thus $P(3)$ is true, and so on.

Let us implement this scheme when $P(n)$ is the statement that

$$1 + 3 + \cdots + (2n-1) = n^2$$

which is a more precise form of the slightly loose statement which began this section. The advantage of the precision is that the mathematics will be cleaner. Here we go.

**Base case**

$P(1)$ is the statement that $1 = 1^2$, which is correct.

**Inductive step**

Now suppose that $r$ is a positive integer and that $P(r)$ is true. Consider the statement $P(r+1)$. We have

$$1 + 3 + \cdots + (2r-1) + (2r+1) = (1 + 3 + \cdots + (2r-1)) + 2r + 1.$$

We are assuming that $P(r)$ is true so

$$1 + 3 + \cdots + (2r-1) = r^2.$$

It follows that

$$1 + 3 + \cdots + (2r-1) + (2r+1) = r^2 + 2r + 1 = (r+1)^2.$$

However, this is exactly what we want, because it asserts that $P(r+1)$ is true. We finish by writing, *by induction, $P(n)$ is true for every positive integer $n$ and the result is proved.*

There are various ways to tinker with this model of an induction proof. For example, you have a statement $P(n)$ which you want to show is true for all integers which are at least $-5$. In this case, you proceed in exactly the same way, but the base case is a check that $P(-5)$ is true and your inductive step works for all $r \geq -5$.

You might want to prove that some statement $P(n)$ is true for all negative integers. Now the base case checks that $P(-1)$ is true, and the inductive step shows that if $r$ is a negative integer, and $P(r)$ is true, then it follows that $P(r-1)$ is true. This time you are running to the left rather than to the right on the number line. If you need to prove a statement $P(n)$ for all integers $n$ by induction, then you need to do two inductions. The base case consists of finding an example of an integer $k$ such that $P(k)$ is true. Then a double strength inductive step shows that if $r$ is an integer such that $P(r)$ is true, then both $P(r+1)$ and $P(r-1)$ are both true. By two inductions, the result is complete.

## Complete induction

Sometimes it is helpful to replace induction by complete induction. To prove a statement $Q(n)$ about the positive integer $n$ by complete induction, you need to do just one thing: *show that, for each positive integer $r$, if $Q(s)$ is true for all positive integers $s$ less than $r$, then $Q(r)$ is true.*

What does that mean? It means, among infinitely many other things, that you are supposed to be able to deduce that $Q(4)$ is true provided that you assume that $Q(1), Q(2)$ and $Q(3)$ are true. Notice that you are required to work out that $Q(1)$ is true on the basis of no assumptions about other statements, which can be done by just spotting that $Q(1)$ is true. On the other hand, you can get away with not bothering to do that check by living dangerously. Provided that you do have a correct argument which shows that *if $Q(s)$ is true for all positive integers $s$ less than $r$, then $Q(r)$ is true*, then you can apply this argument when $r = 1$. This yields a vacuous proof that $Q(1)$ is true since there are no positive integers less than 1. Such serene and dignified self-confidence might make your team leader nervous, and a suspicious mean spirited coordinator might think that you have skipped the base case rather than applied a slick vacuous argument. Be safe. Check that $Q(1)$ is true in case there is something wrong with the $r = 1$ business and label it "unnecessary check". This label is defence against the malign coordinator who wants to argue that you do not understand complete induction because you have done an unnecessary base case!

### Well ordering proofs

One important feature of the positive integers is that every non-empty subset of the positive integers has a least member. The mathematical jargon for this property is to say that the positive integers are *well ordered.* Complete induction proofs can be reorganized as well ordering proofs like this:

We wish to prove that $Q(n)$ is a true statement for all positive integers $n$. Suppose, for contradiction, that there exists a positive integer $k$ such that $Q(k)$ is false. On the basis of this (hopefully false) assumption, you consider the collection of all positive integers $l$ such that $Q(l)$ is false. This set is not empty because $Q(k)$ is false. We may therefore consider the least positive integer $m$ such that $Q(m)$ is false. Now argue that it is impossible for $Q(m)$ to be true if $Q(s)$ is true for all positive integers $s < m$. This is just the same activity as when you set this up as a proof by complete induction. In this well ordering variation of a complete induction proof, you finish by concluding that no such $m$ exists, which is absurd. Therefore the assumption that there exists a positive integer $k$ such that $Q(k)$ is false must have been incorrect. Therefore $Q(n)$ is true for every positive integer $n$.

As you can see, the difference between a complete induction proof and a well ordering proof is largely a matter of organization. A complete induction proof is direct, whereas a well ordering proof involves a proof by contradiction. We will see examples of induction proofs in the next section.

Well ordering proofs are also called *proofs by minimum counterexample.* This is because you derive a contradiction by examining the horrible consequences that would flow from having a minimum counterexample.

## 2.6 Factorization of integers

### The Fundamental Theorem of Arithmetic

Suppose that $m$ and $n$ are integers (this includes positive and negative whole numbers, and zero). We say that *$m$ divides $n$* when there is an integer $d$ such that $n = md$. In this case we also say that $m$ is a *factor* or *divisor* of $n$ and write $m \mid n$. Notice that 0 is divisible by all integers, but the only integer which 0 divides is 0.

There are various elementary properties of division which follow from the definition. For example, if $k, m$ and $n$ are integers such that both $k \mid m$ and $m \mid n$, then $k \mid n$. Also if $m$ and $n$ are integers such that $m \mid n$ and $n \mid m$, then either $m = n$ or $m = -n$.

If $m$ is an integer, then a *multiple* of $m$ is a number of the form $km$ where $k$ is an integer. Thus the multiples of $m$ are precisely the integers which $m$ divides.

A prime number $p$ is a positive integer which is divisible by exactly two positive integers. This definition ensures that 2, 3, 5 and 7 are all prime numbers, but $-7, -1, 1, 4$ and 6 are not.

**Lemma 2.1** *If $m$ is a positive integer and $m > 1$, then there is a prime number $p$ such that $p$ divides $m$.*

PROOF Suppose, for contradiction, that this result is false. Therefore there is an $m$ for which the statement is false (a well ordering proof is on the way!). Among all such $m$, choose the smallest one. This $m$ is bigger than 1 and has no prime divisor. Now $m$ is divisible by the different numbers 1 and $m$, and $m$ is not prime else $m$ would have a prime divisor. Therefore $m$ is divisible by at least three positive integers: 1, $m$ and $k$ where $1 < k < m$. The choice of $m$ ensures that there is a prime number $p$ which divides $k$. However, $k$ divides $m$ so $p$ divides $m$. This is absurd, because $m$ was chosen to have no prime divisors. Therefore it is not the case that lemma 2.1 is false, and so it is true. ❑

**Lemma 2.2** *If $m$ is a positive integer and $m > 1$, then there is a finite list of prime numbers $p_1, p_2, \ldots, p_t$ such that $m = p_1 p_2 \cdots p_t$.*

Examples include $12 = 2 \times 2 \times 3$ and $7 = 7$. We allow the list to contain repeated factors, and also we allow it to contain just one prime number.

PROOF Suppose, for contradiction, that this result is false. Therefore there is a positive integer $m > 1$ which is not a product of prime numbers (another well ordering proof is coming up). Among all such $m$, choose the smallest one. This $m$ is bigger than 1 and is neither prime nor a product of prime numbers.

Since $m$ is not a prime number, there are positive integers $u$ and $v$ such that $1 < u, v < m$ and $m = uv$. The choice of $m$ ensures that each of $u$ and

$v$ is either a prime number, or a product of prime numbers, so $m = uv$ is a product of prime numbers. This is absurd, so it is not the case that lemma 2.2 is false. Therefore lemma 2.2 is true. ❑

Suppose that $m$ and $n$ are integers and that it is not the case that $m = n = 0$. Let $\Delta(m,n)$ denote the collection of integers which divide both $m$ and $n$. You can call the members of $\Delta(m,n)$ the *common divisors* of $m$ and $n$. Thus $\Delta(8,12) = \{-4,-2,-1,1,2,4\} = \Delta(12,8)$. Since one of $m$ and $n$ is not zero (say $m \neq 0$), it follows that if $d$ is a common divisor of $m$ and $n$ then $-|m| \leq d \leq |m|$ and so $\Delta(m,n)$ is a finite set. Also notice that if $d$ is in $\Delta(m,n)$, then so is $-d$. It follows that $\Delta(m,n)$ contains at least one positive integer, and so the greatest element of the finite set $\Delta(m,n)$ is a positive integer $g$. We say that $g$ is the greatest common divisor of $m$ and $n$, and write $g = \gcd(m,n)$.

Notice that

$$\begin{aligned}\Delta(m,n) &= \Delta(n,m)\\ &= \Delta(-m,n)\\ &= \Delta(m+n,n)\\ &= \Delta(m-n,n).\end{aligned}$$

If $k$ is an integer then $\Delta(m,n) = (m-kn,n)$.

For example $\Delta(12,8) = \Delta(12-8,8) = \Delta(4,8) = \Delta(8,4) = \Delta(8-2\times 4,4) = \Delta(0,4) = \Delta(4,0)$. Therefore the common divisors of 12 and 8 are the same as the common divisors of 4 and 0. However, every integer divides 0, so the common divisors of 12 and 8 are the divisors of 4, and so are $-4$, $-2$, $-1$, 1, 2 and 4. The greatest common divisor of 8 and 12 is therefore 4 which I expect that you knew already.

More interestingly,

$$\begin{aligned}\Delta(1729,1001) &= \Delta(728,1001) = \Delta(728,1001-728) = \Delta(728,273)\\ &= \Delta(728-2\times 273,273) = \Delta(182,273) = \Delta(182,91)\\ &= \Delta(182-2\times 91,91) = \Delta(0,91).\end{aligned}$$

Therefore the common divisors of 1729, 1001 are $-91$, $-13$, $-7$, $-1$, 1, 7, 13 and 91 and so the greatest common divisor of 1729 and 1001 is 91.

We are using *Euclid's algorithm* to find the gcd of two positive integers $m$ and $n$. The procedure works like this: start with $m$ and $n$ and suppose that $m > n$. Replace $m$ by $m-n$ so consider the integers $m-n$ and $n$.

If the smaller is 0, then stop, otherwise replace the larger by the larger minus the smaller, and carry on in the same fashion. This procedure can be accelerated by replacing $m$ by the non-negative remainder when $m$ is divided by $n$.

The sum of the pair of integers under consideration is always positive but it decreases at every step. It therefore stops after a finite number of iterations. When it stops the numbers are $g$ and 0 where $g > 0$. The greatest common divisor of $g$ and 0 is $g$.

Each iteration leaves the gcd of the pair of numbers under consideration unchanged, so $\gcd(m,n) = g$.

You may find it helpful to look at this another way: if you are considering the pair $m$, $n$ where $m > n \neq 0$, then next consider the pair $n, m \pmod{n}$. Here $m \pmod{n}$—$m$ modulo $n$—is the non-negative remainder when you divide $m$ by $n$.

A feature of the algorithm is that every number which falls under consideration is of the form $\lambda m + \mu n$ where $\lambda$ and $\mu$ are integers. This is because $m$ and $n$ are both of this form, and because when you subtract two numbers of this form, you obtain another number of this form. It follows that $g = \lambda m + \mu n$ for some integers $\lambda$ and $\mu$. You can work out a pair of integers $\lambda$ and $\mu$ which do the job by unpicking Euclid's algorithm.

Let us explain our example:

$$\begin{aligned}
1729 &= 1 \times 1001 + 728 \\
1001 &= 1 \times 728 + 273 \\
728 &= 2 \times 273 + 182 \\
273 &= 1 \times 182 + 91 \\
182 &= 2 \times 91.
\end{aligned}$$

Therefore 91 is the greatest common divisor of 1001 and 1729 and

$$\begin{aligned}
91 &= 273 - 182 \\
&= 273 - (728 - 2 \times 273) \\
&= 3 \times 273 - 728 \\
&= 3 \times (1001 - 728) - 728 \\
&= 3 \times 1001 - 4 \times 728 \\
&= 3 \times 1001 - 4 \times (1729 - 1001) \\
&= 7 \times 1001 - 4 \times 1729.
\end{aligned}$$

Notice that it is easy to verify that no error has crept into our working by checking that $7 \times 1001 - 4 \times 1729 = 91$.

**Lemma 2.3** *Suppose that $m$ and $n$ are integers and that $p$ is a prime number which divides $mn$. Then $p$ divides $m$ or $p$ divides $n$ (and it is possible that $p$ divides both).*

PROOF Suppose, for contradiction, that this lemma is false. Therefore $p$ divides neither $m$ nor $n$. Then gcd $(m, p) = \gcd(n, p) = 1$. By using Euclid's algorithm, there are integers $\lambda_1, \mu_1$, and $\lambda_2, \mu_2$ such that

$$\lambda_1 m + \mu_1 p = 1 = \lambda_2 n + \mu_2 p.$$

Multiplying we find that

$$(\lambda_1\lambda_2)mn + (\lambda_1\mu_2 m + \mu_1\lambda_2 n + \mu_1\mu_2 p)p = 1.$$

This is absurd because the left-hand side is a multiple of $p$ but the right-hand side is not. Therefore the lemma is correct. ❑

**Corollary 2.1** *If $m_1, m_2, \ldots, m_k$ is a list of integers, and $p$ is a prime number which divides $m_1 m_2 \cdots m_k$, then $p$ divides $m_i$ for at least one $i$ in the range $1 \leq i \leq k$.*

Suppose that $m > 1$ is a positive integer, then lemma 2.2 on page 25 ensures that $m$ admits at least one factorization into prime numbers.

**Fundamental theorem of arithmetic** *Suppose that*

$$m = p_1 p_2 \cdots p_s = q_1 q_2 \cdots q_t$$

*are rival factorizations of $m$ into prime numbers, then $s = t$ and the list $q_1$, $q_2$, $\ldots$, $q_t$ is a permutation (rearrangement) of $p_1$, $p_2$, $\ldots$, $p_t$.*

In the case that $m = 1$, this result becomes the statement that the only way to write 1 as the product of prime numbers is as the product of none of them. This result is true by definition or casuistry, depending on your taste.

PROOF We will prove the result by complete induction on $m$ (so we assume that the result holds for all positive integers which are less than $m$). See section 2.5 on page 21. Suppose that $m$ has two prime factorizations

$m = p_1 p_2 \cdots p_s = q_1 q_2 \cdots q_t$. Now $p_1$ divides $q_1 q_2 \cdots q_t$ and corollary 2.1 applies. It follows that $p_1$ divides $q_i$ for some $i$. Rearranging the list of primes $q_j$, we may assume that $p_1$ divides $q_1$. However, $q_1$ is a prime number so $p_1 = q_1$. Divide through by $p_1$ to obtain two factorizations of $\frac{m}{p_1}$. Now $\frac{m}{p_1} < m$ so by hypothesis we have $s - 1 = t - 1$ and $q_2, q_3, \ldots, q_t$ is a permutation (rearrangement) of $p_2, p_3, \ldots, p_t$. The result now follows by induction. ❑

## Consequences for gcds, lcms and divisors

Suppose that $m = p_1^{a_1} p_2^{a_2} \cdots p_k^{a_k}$ and $n = p_1^{b_1} p_2^{b_2} \cdots p_k^{b_k}$ are factorizations of the positive integers $m$ and $n$ into prime numbers. We can read off the greatest common divisor and least common multiple of these numbers from these factorizations. Let $c_i = \min\{a_i, b_i\}$ for each $i$, and $d_i = \max\{a_i, b_i\}$ for each $i$. Notice that $\min\{c, d\} + \max\{c, d\} = c + d$ for all integers $c$ and $d$. The following statements follow:

(i) $\gcd(m, n) = p_1^{c_1} p_2^{c_2} \cdots p_k^{c_k}$;

(ii) $\operatorname{lcm}(m, n) = p_1^{d_1} p_2^{d_2} \cdots p_k^{d_k}$;

(iii) $\gcd(m, n) \times \operatorname{lcm}(m, n) = mn$.

The number of positive integer divisors of $m$ is

$$(a_1 + 1)(a_2 + 1) \cdots (a_k + 1).$$

The sum of the positive divisors of $m$ is

$$(1 + p_1 + \cdots + p_1^{a_1})(1 + p_2 + \cdots + p_2^{a_2}) \cdots (1 + p_k + \cdots + p_k^{a_k})$$

or if you prefer,

$$\prod_{i=1}^{k} \left( \frac{p_i^{a_i+1} - 1}{p_i - 1} \right).$$

## Consequences for roots and rational numbers

Suppose that $u$ and $t$ are positive integers such that $\sqrt[t]{u}$ is a rational number. It follows that $\sqrt[t]{u}$ is an integer.

PROOF Suppose that

$$\sqrt[t]{u} = \frac{m}{n}$$

where $m$ and $n$ are positive integers and it is harmless to assume that $\gcd(m, n) = 1$. Raise both sides of the equation to the power $t$ so $m^t = n^t u$. Now if the prime number $p$ divides $u$, then it divides $m^t$ and so it divides $m$. You can obtain this by using the full force of the Fundamental Theorem of Arithmetic, or with more finesse just deploy corollary 2.1 on page 28. The coprimality of $m$ and $n$ ensures that $p$ does not divide $n$.

Now every prime $p$ which divides $u$ divides $m^t$ to a power which is a multiple of $t$. Therefore $u$ is a $t$-th power. ❑

## 2.7 Chinese remainder theorem

The Chinese remainder theorem can be formulated in many ways, and it admits of generalization in advanced modern algebra. It is often best viewed in terms of (two directional) arithmetic progressions of integers. The theorem says that if you have a finite collection of arithmetic progressions where the common differences of pairs of different progressions are coprime, then the intersection of these arithmetic progressions is an arithmetic progression, the common difference of which is the product of the common differences of the arithmetic progressions being intersected.

For example, consider these (two directional) arithmetic progressions of integers:

$$\ldots, -17, -10, -3, 4, 11, 18, 25, \ldots$$

and

$$\ldots, -13, -1, 11, 23, 35, \ldots$$

The common difference of the first is 7 and of the second is 12 and $\gcd(7, 12) = 1$. The intersection of these progressions (that is, the terms in both) are the members of the arithmetic progression

$$\ldots, -157, -73, 11, 95, 179, \ldots$$

where the common difference is $84 = 7 \times 12$.

If you omit the condition that the common differences be coprime, then it is possible that two arithmetic progressions have empty intersection. For example

$$\ldots, -17, -11, -5, 1, 7, 13, \ldots$$

and

$$\ldots, -30, -16, -2, 12, 26, \ldots$$

have empty intersection because one collection of numbers is odd and the other is even. However, it is the case that, without restriction on the common difference, if two arithmetic progressions of integers intersect, then their intersection is an arithmetic progression.

Now consider the case that you have three arithmetic progressions with common differences which are pairwise coprime. For example

$$\ldots, -5, -3, -1, 1, 3, 5, \ldots$$

$$\ldots, -17, -8, 1, 10, 19, \ldots$$

$$\ldots, -69, 34, 1, 36, 71 \ldots$$

with common differences 2, 9 and 35. The first two should intersect in an arithmetic progression with common difference 18 and they do:

$$\ldots, -35, -17, 1, 19, 37, \ldots$$

with common difference 18. Now 18 is coprime to 35 so the intersection of all three arithmetic progressions is

$$\ldots, -1259, -629, 1, 631, 1261, \ldots$$

Thus this process is well adapted to inductive generalization. We are ready to make a formal statement of the Chinese remainder theorem. The notion of a common difference will be replaced by the idea of a modulus, and the (two directional) arithmetic progressions will be replaced by congruences which define them, but this is only a change of language. The story is not really changed.

Recall that if $a, b$ and $c$ are integers, we write $a \equiv b \bmod c$ to mean that $c$ is a divisor of $a - b$, and we say that *$a$ is congruent to $b$ modulo $c$*.

**Chinese remainder theorem** *Suppose that $n_1$, $n_2$, ..., $n_t$ are positive integers, that $n_i$ and $n_j$ are coprime whenever the subscripts are different, and that the product of the $n_i$ is $n$. Also suppose that $a_1, a_2, \ldots, a_t$ are integers.*

*We are concerned to know if there exist integers $x$ which satisfy the following congruences simultaneously:*

$$\begin{aligned} x &\equiv a_1 \pmod{n_1} \\ x &\equiv a_2 \pmod{n_2} \\ &\vdots \\ x &\equiv a_t \pmod{n_t} \end{aligned}$$

*It follows that there is an integer $x$ such that $x \equiv a_i \pmod{n_i}$ for all $i$ where $1 \leq i \leq t$.*

*An integer $y$ satisfies these congruences if, and only if, $x \equiv y \pmod{n}$.*

PROOF Suppose that $u, v$ are different integers such that $0 \leq u < v < n$ so $0 < v - u < n$. Let $(u_1, u_2, \ldots, u_t)$ be a list of the smallest non-negative remainders when $u$ is divided by $n_1, n_2, \ldots, n_t$ in turn. Let $(v_1, v_2, \ldots, v_t)$ be the corresponding list of remainders when $u$ is replaced by $v$.

Now if the pairwise coprime integers $n_j$ were all to divide $v - u$, then so would their product $n$. Thus there is an $i$ with $1 \leq i \leq t$ such that $n_i$ does not divide $v - u$ and so

$$(u_1, u_2, \ldots, u_t) \neq (v_1, v_2, \ldots, v_t)$$

in the sense that these two lists differ in at least one position. There are $n$ integers $w$ in the range $0 \leq w < n$ and also $n$ possible lists of remainders (there are $n_i$ possible remainders in the $i$-th position). Therefore every possible list of remainders arises from some integer $w$ between 0 and $n - 1$ inclusive. Moreover an integer which differs from $w$ by a multiple of $n$ leaves the same list of remainders as $w$. Therefore the set of integers which leave a given list of remainders is an integer $x$ in the range $0 \leq x < n$ together with the integers which differ from $x$ by a multiple of $n$.

Finally, the integers $a_i$ in the statement give rise to a list of remainders on division by $n_1, n_2, \ldots, n_t$ in turn, and we choose an integer $x$ to be associated with that list of remainders. ❑

You can think of this theorem as being about simultaneous congruences, and then it says that simultaneous congruences to pairwise coprime moduli have a unique solution modulo the product of the moduli.

# Part I

# Problems

# 2002

1. The altitude from one of the vertices of an acute-angled triangle $ABC$ meets the opposite side at $D$. From $D$ perpendiculars $DE$ and $DF$ are drawn to the other two sides.

   Prove that the length $EF$ is the same whichever vertex is chosen.

2. A conference hall has a round table with $n$ chairs. There are $n$ delegates to the conference. The first delegate chooses his or her seat arbitrarily. Thereafter the $(k+1)$th delegate sits $k$ places to the right of the $k$th delegate for $1 \leq k \leq n-1$. No chair can be occupied by more than one delegate.

   Find the set of values of $n$ for which this is possible.

3. Prove that the sequence defined by

$$y_0 = 1, \quad y_{n+1} = \tfrac{1}{2}\left(3y_n + \sqrt{5y_n^2 - 4}\right)$$

   $(n \geq 0)$ consists only of integers.

4. Suppose that $B_1, B_2, \ldots, B_n$ are $n$ spheres of unit radius arranged in such a way that each sphere touches exactly two others externally. Let $P$ be a point outside all these spheres, and let the $n$ points of contact be $C_1, C_2, \ldots, C_n$. The length of the tangent from $P$ to the sphere $B_i$ $(1 \leq i \leq n)$ is denoted $t_i$.

   Prove that the product of the quantities $t_i$ is not more than the product of the distances $PC_i$.

# 2003

1. For each integer $n > 1$, let $p(n)$ denote the largest prime factor of $n$. Determine all triples of distinct positive integers satisfying

   (i) $x, y, z$ are in arithmetic progression and

   (ii) $p(xyz) \leq 3$.

2. Let $ABC$ be a triangle, and let $D$ be a point on $AB$ such that $4AD = AB$. The half-line $l$ is drawn on the same side of $AB$ as $C$, starting from $D$ and making an angle of $\theta$ with $DA$ where $\theta = \angle ACB$.

   If the circumcircle of $ABC$ meets the half-line $l$ at $P$, show that $PB = 2PD$.

3. Let $f \colon \mathbb{N} \to \mathbb{N}$ be a permutation of the set $\mathbb{N}$ of positive integers.

   (a) Show that there is an arithmetic progression of positive integers $a, a+d, a+2d$, where $d > 0$, such that

   $$f(a) < f(a+d) < f(a+2d).$$

   (b) Must there be an arithmetic progression $a, a+d, \ldots, a+2003d$, where $d > 0$, such that

   $$f(a) < f(a+d) < f(a+2d) < \cdots < f(a+2003d)?$$

   *[A permutation of $\mathbb{N}$ is a one-to-one function whose image is the whole of $\mathbb{N}$; that is, a function $f$ from $\mathbb{N}$ to $\mathbb{N}$ such that, for all $m \in \mathbb{N}$ there exists a unique $n \in \mathbb{N}$ such that $f(n) = m$.]*

*/continued ...*

4. Let $f$ be a function from the set of non-negative integers into itself such that for all $n \geq 0$

   (i) $(f(2n+1))^2 - (f(2n))^2 = 6f(n) + 1$ and

   (ii) $f(2n) \geq f(n)$.

   How many numbers less than 2003 are there in the image of $f$?

# 2004

1. Let $ABC$ be an equilateral triangle and $D$ be an internal point of the side $BC$. A circle, tangent to $BC$ at $D$, cuts $AB$ internally at $M$ and $N$, and $AC$ internally at $P$ and $Q$.

   Show that $BD + AM + AN = CD + AP + AQ$.

2. Show that there is an integer $n$ with the following properties:

   (i) the binary expansion of $n$ has precisely 2004 0s and 2004 1s;

   (ii) 2004 divides $n$.

3. (a) Given real numbers $a$, $b$ and $c$ with $a + b + c = 0$, prove that $a^3 + b^3 + c^3 > 0$ if, and only if, $a^5 + b^5 + c^5 > 0$.

   (b) Given real numbers $a$, $b$, $c$ and $d$ with $a + b + c + d = 0$, prove that $a^3 + b^3 + c^3 + d^3 > 0$ if, and only if, $a^5 + b^5 + c^5 + d^5 > 0$.

4. The real number $x$ between 0 and 1 has decimal representation

   $$0.a_1a_2a_3a_4\ldots$$

   and enjoys the following property: the number of *distinct* blocks of the form

   $$a_ka_{k+1}a_{k+2}\cdots a_{k+2003},$$

   as $k$ ranges through the positive integers, is less than or equal to 2004.

   Prove that $x$ is rational.

# 2005

1. The integer $N$ is positive. There are exactly 2005 ordered pairs $(x, y)$ of positive integers satisfying

$$\frac{1}{x} + \frac{1}{y} = \frac{1}{N}.$$

Prove that $N$ is a perfect square.

2. In triangle $ABC$, $\angle BAC = 120°$. Let the angle bisectors of angles $A$, $B$ and $C$ meet the opposite sides in $D$, $E$ and $F$ respectively.

Prove that the circle on diameter $EF$ passes through $D$.

3. Let $a$, $b$, $c$ be positive real numbers. Prove that

$$\left(\frac{a}{b} + \frac{b}{c} + \frac{c}{a}\right)^2 \geq (a + b + c)\left(\frac{1}{a} + \frac{1}{b} + \frac{1}{c}\right).$$

4. Let $X = \{A_1, A_2, \ldots, A_n\}$ be a set of distinct 3-element subsets of $\{1, 2, \ldots, 36\}$ such that

   (i) $A_i$ and $A_j$ have non-empty intersection for every $i, j$ and

   (ii) the intersection of all the elements of $X$ is the empty set.

   (a) Show that $n \leq 100$.

   (b) How many such sets $X$ are there when $n = 100$?

# 2006

1. Find the minimum possible value of $x^2 + y^2$ given that $x$ and $y$ are real numbers satisfying

$$xy(x^2 - y^2) = x^2 + y^2 \text{ and } x \neq 0.$$

2. Let $x$ and $y$ be positive integers with no prime factors larger than 5.

   Find all such $x$ and $y$ which satisfy

$$x^2 - y^2 = 2^k$$

   for some non-negative integer $k$.

3. Let $ABC$ be a triangle with $AC > AB$. The point $X$ lies on the side $BA$ extended through $A$, and the point $Y$ lies on the side $CA$ in such a way that $BX = CA$ and $CY = BA$. The line $XY$ meets the perpendicular bisector of side $BC$ at $P$.

   Show that

$$\angle BPC + \angle BAC = 180°.$$

4. An exam consisting of six questions is sat by 2006 children. Each question is marked either right or wrong. Any three children have right answers to at least five of the six questions between them.

   Let $N$ be the total number of right answers achieved by all the children, that is, (the total number of questions solved by child 1) + (the total solved by child 2) $+ \cdots +$ (the total solved by child 2006).

   Find the least possible value of $N$.

# 2007

1. Triangle $ABC$ has integer-length sides, and $AC = 2007$. The internal bisector of $\angle BAC$ meets $BC$ at $D$.

   Given that $AB = CD$, determine $AB$ and $BC$.

2. Show that there are infinitely many pairs of positive integers $(m, n)$ such that

   $$\frac{m+1}{n} + \frac{n+1}{m}$$

   is a positive integer.

3. Let $ABC$ be an acute-angled triangle with $AB > AC$ and $\angle BAC = 60°$. Denote the circumcentre by $O$ and the orthocentre by $H$ and let $OH$ meet $AB$ at $P$ and $AC$ at $Q$.

   Prove that $PO = HQ$.

   *[The* circumcentre *of triangle ABC is the centre of the circle which passes through the vertices A, B and C. The* orthocentre *is the point of intersection of the perpendiculars from each vertex to the opposite side.]*

4. In the land of Hexagonia, the six cities are connected by a rail network such that there is a direct rail line connecting each pair of cities. On Sundays, some lines may be closed for repair. The passengers' rail charter stipulates that any city must be accessible by rail from any other (not necessarily directly) at all times.

   In how many different ways can some of the lines be closed subject to this condition?

# 2008

1. Find the minimum value of $x^2 + y^2 + z^2$, where $x$, $y$, $z$ are real numbers such that $x^3 + y^3 + z^3 - 3xyz = 1$.

2. Let triangle $ABC$ have incentre $I$ and circumcentre $O$. Suppose that $\angle AIO = 90°$ and $\angle CIO = 45°$.

   Find the ratio $AB : BC : CA$.

   *[The* circumcentre *of triangle ABC is the centre of the circle which passes through the vertices A, B and C. The* incentre *is the centre of the circle which touches the sides AB, BC and CA.]*

3. Adrian has drawn a circle in the $xy$-plane whose radius is a positive integer at most 2008. The origin lies somewhere inside the circle.

   You are allowed to ask him questions of the form "Is the point $(x, y)$ inside your circle?" After each question he will answer truthfully "yes" or "no".

   Show that it is always possible to deduce the radius of the circle after at most sixty questions.

   *[Any point which lies exactly on the circle may be considered to lie inside the circle.]*

4. Prove that there are infinitely many pairs of distinct positive integers $x$, $y$ such that $x^2 + y^3$ is divisible by $x^3 + y^2$.

# 2009

1. Find all solutions in non-negative integers $a, b$ to $\sqrt{a} + \sqrt{b} = \sqrt{2009}$.

2. Let $ABC$ be an acute-angled triangle with $\angle B = \angle C$. Let the circumcentre be $O$ and the orthocentre be $H$.

   Prove that the centre of the circle $BOH$ lies on the line $AB$.

   *[The* circumcentre *of triangle $ABC$ is the centre of the circle which passes through the vertices $A$, $B$ and $C$. The* orthocentre *is the point of intersection of the perpendiculars from each vertex to the opposite side.]*

3. Find all functions $f$ from the real numbers to the real numbers which satisfy

$$f(x^3) + f(y^3) = (x + y)(f(x^2) + f(y^2) - f(xy))$$

   for all real numbers $x$ and $y$.

4. Given a positive integer $n$, let $b(n)$ denote the number of positive integers whose binary representations occur as blocks of consecutive integers in the binary expansion of $n$. For example, $b(13) = 6$ because $13 = 1101_2$, which contains as consecutive blocks the binary representations of $13 = 1101_2$, $6 = 110_2$, $5 = 101_2$, $3 = 11_2$, $2 = 10_2$ and $1 = 1_2$.

   Show that if $n \leq 2500$, then $b(n) \leq 39$; determine the values of $n$ for which equality holds.

# 2010

1. There are $2010^{2010}$ children at a mathematics camp. Each has at most three friends at the camp, and if $A$ is friends with $B$, then $B$ is friends with $A$.

   The camp leader would like to line the children up so that there are at most 2010 children between any pair of friends. Is it always possible to do this?

2. In triangle $ABC$ the centroid is $G$ and $D$ is the midpoint of $CA$. The line through $G$ parallel to $BC$ meets $AB$ at $E$.

   Prove that $\angle AEC = \angle DGC$ if, and only if, $\angle ACB = 90°$.

   *[The* centroid *of a triangle is the point of intersection of the three medians. A* median *joins a vertex to the midpoint of the opposite side.]*

3. The integer $x$ is at least 3 and $n = x^6 - 1$. Let $p$ be a prime and $k$ be a positive integer such that $p^k$ is a factor of $n$.

   Show that $p^{3k} < 8n$.

4. Prove that, for all positive real numbers $x$, $y$ and $z$,

$$4(x+y+z)^3 > 27(x^2y + y^2z + z^2x).$$

# 2011

1. Let $ABC$ be a triangle and $X$ be a point inside the triangle. The lines $AX$, $BX$ and $CX$ meet the circle $ABC$ again at $P$, $Q$ and $R$ respectively.

   Choose a point $U$ on $XP$ which is between $X$ and $P$. Suppose that the lines through $U$ which are parallel to $AB$ and $CA$ meet $XQ$ and $XR$ at points $V$ and $W$ respectively.

   Prove that the points $R$, $W$, $V$ and $Q$ lie on a circle.

2. Find all positive integers $x$ and $y$ such that $x+y+1$ divides $2xy$ and $x+y-1$ divides $x^2+y^2-1$.

3. The function $f$ is defined on the positive integers as follows:

$$f(1) = 1;$$

$$f(2n) = \begin{cases} f(n) & \text{if } n \text{ is even;} \\ 2f(n) & \text{if } n \text{ is odd;} \end{cases}$$

$$f(2n+1) = \begin{cases} 2f(n)+1 & \text{if } n \text{ is even;} \\ f(n) & \text{if } n \text{ is odd.} \end{cases}$$

   Find the number of positive integers $n$ which are less than 2011 and have the property that $f(n) = f(2011)$.

*/continued ...*

4. Let $G$ be the set of points $(x, y)$ in the plane such that $x$ and $y$ are integers in the range $1 \leq x, y \leq 2011$. A subset $S$ of $G$ is said to be *parallelogram-free* if there is no proper parallelogram with all its vertices in $S$.

   Determine the largest possible size of a parallelogram-free subset of $G$.

   *[A* proper parallelogram *is one where its vertices do not all lie on the same line.]*

# 2012

1. The diagonals $AC$ and $BD$ of a cyclic quadrilateral meet at $E$. The midpoints of the sides $AB$, $BC$, $CD$ and $DA$ are $P$, $Q$, $R$ and $S$ respectively.

   Prove that the circles $EPS$ and $EQR$ have the same radius.

2. A function $f$ is defined on the positive integers by $f(1) = 1$ and, for $n > 1$,

   $$f(n) = f\left(\left\lfloor \frac{2n-1}{3} \right\rfloor\right) + f\left(\left\lfloor \frac{2n}{3} \right\rfloor\right)$$

   where $\lfloor x \rfloor$ denotes the greatest integer less than or equal to $x$.

   Is it true that $f(n) - f(n-1) \leq n$ for all $n > 1$?

   *[Here are some examples of the use of $\lfloor x \rfloor$: $\lfloor \pi \rfloor = 3$; $\lfloor 1729 \rfloor = 1729$; $\left\lfloor \frac{2012}{1000} \right\rfloor = 2$.]*

3. The set of real numbers is split into two subsets which do not intersect.

   Prove that for each pair $(m, n)$ of positive integers, there are real numbers $x < y < z$ all in the same subset such that $m(z - y) = n(y - x)$.

4. Show that there is a positive integer $k$ with the following property: if $a$, $b$, $c$, $d$, $e$ and $f$ are integers and $m$ is a divisor of

   $$a^n + b^n + c^n - d^n - e^n - f^n$$

   for all integers $n$ in the range $1 \leq n \leq k$, then $m$ is a divisor of $a^n + b^n + c^n - d^n - e^n - f^n$ for all positive integers $n$.

# 2013

1. Are there infinitely many pairs of positive integers $(m, n)$ such that both $m$ divides $n^2 + 1$ and $n$ divides $m^2 + 1$?

2. The point $P$ lies inside triangle $ABC$ so that $\angle ABP = \angle PCA$. The point $Q$ is such that $PBQC$ is a parallelogram.

   Prove that $\angle QAB = \angle CAP$.

3. Consider the set of positive integers which, when written in binary, have exactly 2013 digits and more 0s than 1s. Let $n$ be the number of such integers and let $s$ be their sum.

   Prove that, when written in binary, $n + s$ has more 0s than 1s.

4. Suppose that $ABCD$ is a square and that $P$ is a point which is on the circle inscribed in the square.

   Determine whether or not it is possible that $PA$, $PB$, $PC$, $PD$ and $AB$ are all integers.

# 2014

1. Every diagonal of a regular polygon with 2014 sides is coloured in one of $n$ colours. Whenever two diagonals cross in the interior, they are of different colours.

   What is the minimum value of $n$ for which this is possible?

2. Prove that it is impossible to have a cuboid for which the volume, the surface area and the perimeter are numerically equal.

   *[The* perimeter of a cuboid *is the sum of the lengths of all its twelve edges.]*

3. Let $a_0 = 4$ and define a sequence of terms using the formula $a_n = a_{n-1}^2 - a_{n-1}$ for each positive integer $n$.

   (a) Prove that there are infinitely many prime numbers which are factors of at least one term in the sequence;

   (b) Are there infinitely many prime numbers which are factors of no term in the sequence?

4. Let $ABC$ be a triangle and $P$ be a point in its interior.

   Let $AP$ meet the circumcircle of $ABC$ again at $A'$. The points $B'$ and $C'$ are similarly defined.

   Let $O_A$ be the circumcentre of $BCP$. The circumcentres $O_B$ and $O_C$ are similarly defined.

   Let $Q_A$ be the circumcentre of $B'C'P$. The circumcentres $Q_B$ and $Q_C$ are similarly defined.

   Prove that the lines $O_AQ_A, O_BQ_B$ and $O_CQ_C$ are concurrent.

# 2015

1. The first term $x_1$ of a sequence is 2014. Each subsequent term of the sequence is defined in terms of the previous term. The iterative formula is

$$x_{n+1} = \frac{(\sqrt{2}+1)x_n - 1}{(\sqrt{2}+1) + x_n}.$$

Find the 2015th term $x_{2015}$.

2. In Oddesdon Primary School there are an odd number of classes. Each class contains an odd number of pupils. One pupil from each class will be chosen to form the school council.

Prove that the following two statements are logically equivalent.

(i) There are more ways to form a school council which includes an odd number of boys than ways to form a school council which includes an odd number of girls.

(ii) There are an odd number of classes which contain more boys than girls.

3. Two circles touch one another internally at $A$. A variable chord $PQ$ of the outer circle touches the inner circle.

Prove that the locus of the incentre of triangle $AQP$ is another circle touching the given circles at $A$.

*[The* incentre *of triangle $ABC$ is the centre of the circle which touches the sides $AB$, $BC$ and $CA$. A* locus *is the collection of all points which satisfy a given condition.]*

*/continued ...*

4. Given two points $P$ and $Q$ with integer coordinates, we say that $P$ *sees* $Q$ if the line segment $PQ$ contains no other points with integer coordinates. An *n-loop* is a sequence of $n$ points $P_1, P_2, \ldots, P_n$, each with integer coordinates, such that the following conditions hold:

   (i) $P_j$ sees $P_{j+1}$ for $1 \leq j \leq n-1$, and $P_n$ sees $P_1$;

   (ii) No $P_j$ sees any $P_k$ apart from those mentioned in (a);

   (iii) No three of the points lie on the same straight line.

   Does there exist a 100-loop?

# 2016

1. Circles of radius $r_1$, $r_2$ and $r_3$ touch each other externally, and they touch a common tangent at points $A$, $B$ and $C$ respectively, where $B$ lies between $A$ and $C$.

   Prove that $16(r_1 + r_2 + r_3) \geq 9(AB + BC + CA)$.

2. Alison has compiled a list of 20 hockey teams, ordered by how good she thinks they are, but refuses to share it. Benjamin may mention three teams to her, and she will then choose either to tell him which she thinks is the weakest team of the three, or which she thinks is the strongest team of the three. Benjamin may do this as many times as he likes.

   Determine the largest $N$ such that Benjamin can guarantee to be able to find a sequence $T_1, T_2, \ldots, T_N$ of teams with the property that he knows that Alison thinks that $T_i$ is better than $T_{i+1}$ for each $1 \leq i < N$.

3. Let $ABCD$ be a cyclic quadrilateral. The diagonals $AC$ and $BD$ meet at $P$, and $DA$ and $CB$ produced meet at $Q$. The midpoint of $AB$ is $E$.

   Prove that if $PQ$ is perpendicular to $AC$, then $PE$ is perpendicular to $BC$.

4. Suppose that $p$ is a prime number and that there are different positive integers $u$ and $v$ such that $p^2$ is the mean of $u^2$ and $v^2$.

   Prove that $2p - u - v$ is a square or twice a square.

# Fictional IMO

1. A $2n \times 2n$ board is divided into $4n^2$ small squares in the manner of a chessboard. Each small square is painted with one of four colours so that every $2 \times 2$ block of four small squares involves all four colours.

   Prove that the four corner squares of the board are painted with different colours.

2. Which positive integers $n$ have the property that $\{1, 2, \ldots, n\}$ can be partitioned into two subsets $A$ and $B$ so that the sum of the squares of the elements of $A$ is the sum of the squares of the elements of $B$?

3. This problem concerns polynomials in $x$ with real coefficients.

   Let $f(x) = 2013x + 1$. Suppose that $g(x)$ and $h(x)$ are polynomials such that $f(g(x)) = g(f(x))$ and $f(h(x)) = h(f(x))$.
   Prove that $g(h(x)) = h(g(x))$.

# Part II

# Solutions

# 2002 solutions

## Problem 1

The altitude from one of the vertices of an acute-angled triangle $ABC$ meets the opposite side at $D$. From $D$ perpendiculars $DE$ and $DF$ are drawn to the other two sides.

Prove that the length $EF$ is the same whichever vertex is chosen.

*[Christopher Bradley, ex-Clifton College]*

### Discussion

This delightful result will surely come as a surprise to many readers. In fact there are many ways to solve this problem, including a very attractive trigonometric route. Hesitate to spurn a trigonometric path that is well paved with right-angled triangles, for you are certain to be able to make progress.

Perhaps now is a good moment to remind ourselves of the sine rule and its relationship to an elegant triangle area formula. Suppose that triangle $ABC$ has side lengths $a$, $b$ and $c$ opposite angles $A$, $B$ and $C$.

The sine rule states that

$$\frac{a}{\sin A} = \frac{b}{\sin B} = \frac{c}{\sin C} = 2R,$$

where $2R$ is the diameter of the circumcircle of $ABC$. A well-known formula for the area $[ABC]$ of this triangle is

$$[ABC] = \tfrac{1}{2}ab\sin C, \tag{3.1}$$

and there are two more similar formulas obtained by cyclically permuting the first three letters of the alphabet. Now, by the sine rule,

$$\frac{c}{\sin C} = 2R,$$

or better yet

$$\sin C = \frac{c}{2R}.$$

We can use this to remove the offending trigonometric function from equation (3.1) and obtain the beautiful triangle area formula

$$[ABC] = \frac{abc}{4R}.$$

However, trigonometric functions should enjoy their day in the sun, and we can insert them into this formula using $a = 2R \sin A$ (and two similar expressions) to discover that

$$[ABC] = 2R^2 \sin A \sin B \sin C. \tag{3.2}$$

We suppose that the perpendicular is dropped from the vertex $A$ with $E$ on $CA$ and $F$ on $AB$. If you want to use similar triangles, there is a rich supply. After a little angle chasing we obtain the following triangle similarities:

$$ADC \sim AED \sim DEC \quad \text{and} \quad ABD \sim DBF \sim ADF.$$

Although we have a general policy of describing triangles anticlockwise, there are some indirect similarities here, and these trump our anticlockwise preference. See figure 3.1.

By slightly more devious angle-chasing, involving the cyclic quadrilateral $AFDE$, we have the similarity

$$ABC \sim AEF.$$

## Solution

We will give several solutions. We suppose that the perpendicular is dropped from the vertex $A$, and we will try to demonstrate that the length $EF$ would be the same if we replaced $A$ by $B$ or $C$.

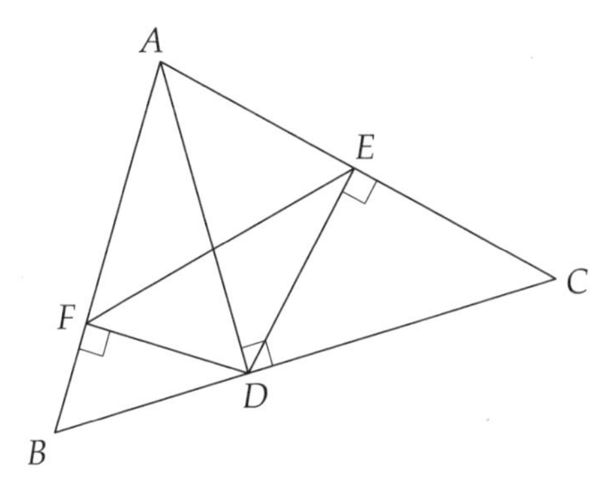


*Figure 3.1*

**Solution 1**

The circle on diameter $AD$ passes through $E$ and $F$ by the converse of angle in a semicircle (Thales). Apply the sine rule to learn that $EF = AD \sin A$. Triangle $ABD$ has a right angle at $D$ and so $AD = AB \sin B$. Let the radius of the circumcircle of triangle $ABC$ be $R$, and apply the sine rule to obtain that $AB = 2R \sin C$. Putting all this together, it follows that

$$EF = 2R \sin A \sin B \sin C.$$

The quantity on the right is invariant (unchanged) under cyclic permutation of the letters $A$, $B$ and $C$, so the result is established.

It is worth pressing on just a little. In the discussion preceding this solution, we observed that the area of triangle $ABC$ is given by equation (3.2) and so

$$EF = \frac{[ABC]}{R}.$$

This is another formula which is invariant under cyclic permutation of the letters $A$, $B$ and $C$. We only point this out because the area and circumradius of a triangle are perhaps more concrete attributes of a triangle than trigonometric functions of its angles.

**Solution 2**

Notice that

$$\angle DCA + \angle CAD = 90^\circ = \angle ADE + \angle EAD = \angle ADE + \angle CAD$$

and so $\angle C = \angle ADE$ and similarly $\angle B = \angle FDA$. Now $\angle A + \angle B + \angle C = 180°$ so $AFDE$ is a cyclic quadrilateral (as in solution 1) and therefore $\angle FEA = \angle B$ and $\angle AFE = \angle C$ by angles in the same segment.

It follows that $CEFB$ is a cyclic quadrilateral. The triangles $AEF$ and $ABC$ are (indirectly) similar by angle considerations.

Therefore

$$\frac{EF}{BC} = \frac{AF}{AC}$$

and so

$$EF \times AB \times CA = AF \times AB \times BC = AE \times BC \times CA. \tag{3.3}$$

Notice that $\angle CED$ is a right angle, so by the converse of the theorem of Thales (angle in a semicircle), $DC$ is a diameter of circle $CED$, and $AD$ is a tangent to this circle. Therefore $AD^2 = AE \times AC$ by the tangent-secant theorem (see section 2.2 on page 16). Similarly $AF \times AB = AD^2$ so $AF \times AB = AE \times AC$. This justifies the final equality in equation (3.3).

Therefore

$$EF \times AB \times BC \times CA = AD^2 \times BC^2 = 4[ABC]^2.$$

By cyclically permuting the letters $A$, $B$ and $C$, the proof is complete.

**Solution 3**

The theorem of Ptolemy states that the product of the diagonals of a cyclic quadrilateral is the sum of the products of its opposite sides. See figure 3.2, where $hk = xz + wy$.

We can apply this to the cyclic quadrilateral $AFDE$ of figure 3.1 on page 71 to discover that

$$EF \times AD = AF \times ED + AE \times FD.$$

We will reuse the tangent-secant trick used in solution 2, the fact that $AF \times AB = AE \times AC = AD^2$. We have

$$\begin{aligned} EF \times AD \times AB \times AC &= AF \times ED \times AB \times AC + AE \times FD \times AB \times AC \\ &= AD^2 \times ED \times AC + AD^2 \times FD \times AB \\ &= AD^2 \times (2[ADC] + 2[ABD]) \\ &= 2 \times AD^2 \times [ABC]. \end{aligned}$$

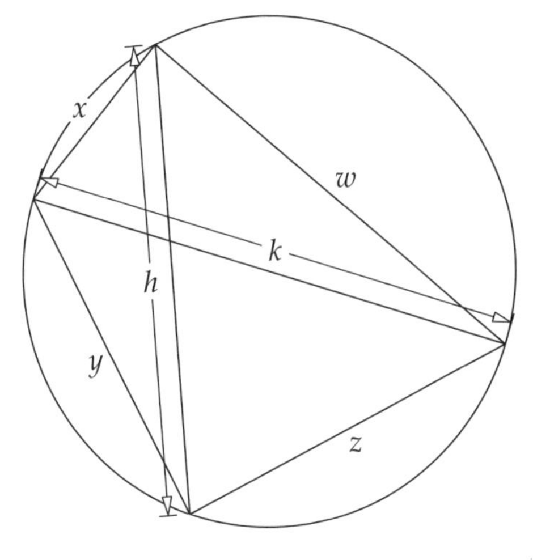


*Figure 3.2*

We have employed the "half base times height" formula for the area of a triangle. Now multiply by $BC^2$ to obtain

$$EF \times AB \times BC \times CA \times 2[ABC] = 8[ABC]^3$$

and so

$$EF \times AB \times BC \times CA = 4[ABC]^2.$$

Once again we finish by cyclically permuting $A$, $B$ and $C$.

**Solution 4**

Candidates who have figure 3.3 on the following page loaded in their minds for immediate use may be tempted by a trigonometric calculation.

The altitudes of a triangle (illustrated in figure 3.3) generate a diagram with many line segments, all of which have lengths given by simple trigonometric formulas. The distance $EF = R \sin 2A$. This standard result can be quoted. It can be derived either by applying Ptolemy's theorem to our cyclic quadrilateral inscribed in the circle on diameter $AH$, or, with a touch more class (if you know the theory of the nine-point circle mentioned in section 2.3) use the sine rule on the orthic triangle.

We digress in case this is an unfamiliar object. The three altitudes of triangle $ABC$ meet at its orthocentre $H$. The feet of these three altitudes are

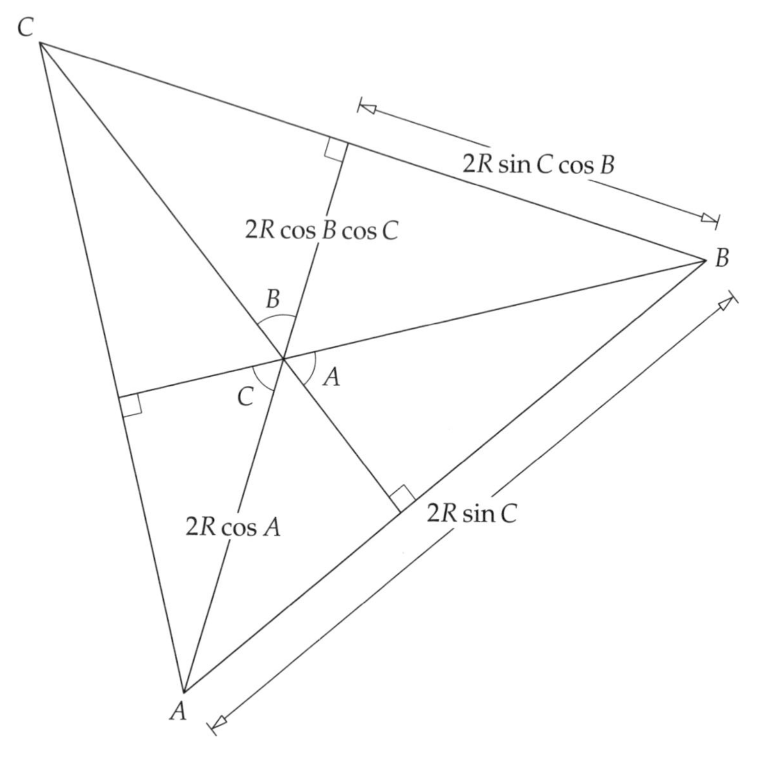


*Figure 3.3*

the vertices of the *orthic triangle* of triangle $ABC$. When $ABC$ is an acute-angled triangle, the angles of the orthic triangle are the supplements of $2A$, $2B$ and $2C$ located in natural positions. The circumcircle of the orthic triangle is the nine-point circle of triangle $ABC$, and this has diameter $R$. Incidentally, if $ABC$ were an obtuse triangle, matters would be slightly more delicate, and we leave the reader to investigate its angles.

If you happen to know all that, and there are people who do, then you have the option of mixing trigonometry with an enlargement. The line segment $EF$ is the enlargement from $A$ of the corresponding side of the orthic triangle of length $R\sin 2A$. The scale factor of the enlargement is the height of triangle $ABC$ (viewed as having base $BC$) divided by $AH$. Therefore

$$EF = R\sin 2A \times \frac{2R\sin B\sin C}{2R\cos A} = 2R\sin A\sin B\sin C,$$

and this is unchanged by cyclic change of letters.

# Problem 2

A conference hall has a round table with $n$ chairs. There are $n$ delegates to the conference. The first delegate chooses his or her seat arbitrarily. Thereafter the $(k+1)$th delegate sits $k$ places to the right of the $k$th delegate for $1 \le k \le n-1$. No chair can be occupied by more than one delegate.

Find the set of values of $n$ for which this is possible.

*[Alan West, University of Leeds]*

## Discussion

If you perform some numerical experiments, preferably using arithmetic modulo $n$ to keep the numbers in check, then you should find that the first few small numbers $n$ for which the seating arrangements are satisfactory are 1, 2, 4 and 8. That should suggest a conjecture.

## Solution

Label the chairs $0, 1, 2, \ldots$ in anticlockwise cyclic order, deeming the first delegate to sit in chair 0, the second in chair 1, the third in chair $1+2$ and so on. Delegate $k+1$ sits in chair $1+2+\cdots+k$. Note that arithmetic is done modulo $n$ here.

The $k$th delegate will sit in chair $\binom{k}{2}$ where we are using this notation to describe a binomial coefficient which occurs in *Pascal's triangle*. You might think that we have to deal with the first delegate ($k=0$) separately, but the formula for binomial coefficients works correctly even in that case because $\binom{0}{2} = \dfrac{0(0-1)}{2} = 0$.

Things will go wrong precisely when there are two different numbers $p$ and $q$ in the range $1 \le p < q \le n$ such that

$$\binom{p}{2} \equiv \binom{q}{2} \pmod{n}.$$

Now $p(p-1) - q(q-1) = (p+q-1)(p-q)$. We have a clash of seating ambitions if, and only if,

$$(q-p)(p+q-1) \equiv 0 \pmod{2n}.$$

Suppose that $2n = uv$ is not a power of 2, where one of $u$ and $v$ is odd (and bigger than 1) and the other is a proper power of 2 (and we carefully refrain from saying which is which). Each of $u$ and $v$ is at most $n$ because one of them is odd (and so must divide $n$) and the other is at most $2n/3$ because $n$ has an odd prime factor. We may suppose that $u > v$. Let $p = (u - v + 1)/2$ and $q = (u + v + 1)/2$, different positive integers no bigger than $n$. This definition is arranged so that $u = p + q - 1$ and $v = q - p$.

Now

$$(q - p)(p + q - 1) = 2n$$

and so

$$\binom{p}{2} = \binom{q}{2} \pmod{2n}.$$

We have manufactured the required embarrassing incident with delegates $p$ and $q$ squabbling over the same chair with $p < q$.

On the other hand, suppose that $2n$ is a power of 2, and (for contradiction) that delegates $p$ and $q$ have conflicting ambitions (with $p < q$) so that $2n$ is a factor of $(q - p)(p + q - 1)$. Notice that exactly one of the factors $p + q - 1$ and $q - p$ is even so $2n$ must divide that factor. Now $0 < q - p < n$ so there can be no seating clash unless $2n$ divides $p + q - 1$. However, $0 < p + q - 1 < 2q - 1 < 2n$. This is absurd and so there can be no ugly seating disputes.

## Afterword

There is a whole family of problems that can be made by fiddling with this question. Simply vary the rule which is used to determine where delegate $k$ sits.

# Problem 3

Prove that the sequence defined by

$$y_0 = 1, \quad y_{n+1} = \tfrac{1}{2}\left(3y_n + \sqrt{5y_n^2 - 4}\right)$$

$(n \geq 0)$ consists only of integers.

*[Christopher Bradley, ex-Clifton College]*

## Discussion

Somehow, this inductive recipe inevitably produces integers $y_i$ with the property that $5y_i^2 - 4$ is a square.

We will give a proof which involves the discussion of roots of polynomials. There is some controversy as to how polynomials should be written, and how the word *root* is used. The expression $x^2 - 3x + 2$ is an uncontroversial example of a polynomial in $x$. Some people like to use a capital letter for the 'unknown' or 'variable' quantity, and would prefer to write this polynomial as $X^2 - 3X + 2$. However, I have been warned that this would inspire wailing, gnashing of teeth and possibly insurrection, so let us stick with the small letter $x$. If you want to give the expression $x^2 - 3x + 2$ a snappy name, you might call it $p$, or possibly you might call it $p(x)$ to remind yourself that it can be regarded as a function of $x$.

Then there is the issue of how to use the word *root*. For example, it is uncontroversial to write $p(2) = 0$. However, should we say that 2 is a root of the equation $x^2 - 3x + 2 = 0$ or do we say that 2 is a root of the polynomial $x^2 - 3x + 2$? I am definitely in the second camp, and view roots as being associated with polynomials rather than equations.

## Solution

We give two solutions. The first one is entirely naive; you spot a pattern and prove that it works. The second method is altogether more stylish, and involves two roots of a quadratic polynomial.

**Solution 1**

We begin with a pedestrian proof. After performing some calculations, you should discover that the sequence $y_0, y_1, y_2, \ldots$ begins

$$1, 2, 5, 13, \ldots.$$

At this point, our stroll through this problem should be interrupted by flashing lights and wailing sirens coming down the road. You ought to suspect that these numbers are alternate terms of the *Fibonacci sequence*

$$0, 1, 1, 2, 3, 5, 8, 13, 21, 34, \ldots.$$

Here $F_0 = 0, F_1 = 1$ and for $n \geq 2$, $F_n = F_{n-1} + F_{n-2}$. It seems likely that $y_i = F_{2i+1}$ for each $i$.

We need to show that

$$F_{2n+3} = \tfrac{1}{2}\left(3F_{2n+1} + \sqrt{5F_{n+1}^2 - 4}\right)$$

for $n \geq 0$ which is equivalent to

$$(2F_{2n+3} - 3F_{2n+1})^2 = 5F_{n+1}^2 - 4 \text{ and } 2F_{2n+3} - 3F_{2n+1} > 0.$$

However, $2F_{2n+3} = 2F_{2n+2} + 2F_{2n+1} = F_{2n+2} + 3F_{2n+1} + F_{2n}$ so $2F_{2n+3} - 3F_{2n+1} = F_{2n+2} + F_{2n} > 0$ for $n \geq 0$. We just need to prove that

$$(2F_{2n+3} - 3F_{2n+1})^2 = 5F_{n+1}^2 - 4,$$

or equivalently (rearranging and dividing through by 4) that

$$F_{2n+3}^2 - 3F_{2n+3}F_{2n+1} + F_{2n+1}^2 + 1 = 0.$$

This just says that

$$(F_{2n+3} - F_{2n+1})^2 - F_{2n+3}F_{2n+1} + 1 = 0$$

or rather

$$F_{2n+2}^2 = F_{2n+3}F_{2n+1} - 1$$

for every $n \geq 0$.

This a is a well-known fact, and follows from the more general Cassini identity which asserts that $F_{k+1}^2 = F_{k+2}F_k + (-1)^k$ for all $k \geq 0$. This can either be quoted or proved by induction on $k$. See section 2.5 on page 21.

**Solution 2**

By direct calculation, $y_0 = 1$ and $y_1 = 2$. Eliminating the square root symbol from the equation in the question, we obtain

$$y_{n+1}^2 - 3y_{n+1}y_n + y_n^2 + 1 = 0.$$

For $n > 1$, this means that $y_{n+1}$ is a root of $x^2 - 3y_n x + (y_n^2 + 1)$ and (decrementing the subscript by 1) $y_n$ is a root of $x^2 - 3y_{n-1}x + (y_{n-1}^2 + 1)$. This second fact means that we get 0 if we substitute $y_n$ for $x$. We can reinterpret that as saying that $y_{n-1}$ is a root of $y_n^2 - 3y_n x + (x^2 + 1)$, that is to say, $y_{n-1}$ is a root of $x^2 - 3y_n x + (y_n^2 + 1)$. Both $y_{n-1}$ and $y_{n+1}$ are roots of the same polynomial $x^2 - 3y_n x + (y_n^2 + 1)$, and $y_{n-1}$ and $y_{n+1}$ are different because the sequence $(y_i)$ is strictly increasing given the inductive definition of $y_{n+1}$ supplied in the question. Therefore we have found both the roots of the quadratic $x^2 - 3y_n x + (y_n^2 + 1)$ and so, since $-3y_n$ is the coefficient of $x$, it follows that $y_{n-1} + y_{n+1} = 3y_n$. Put another way,

$$y_{n+1} = 3y_n - y_{n-1} \tag{3.4}$$

for $n \geq 1$. Each term $y_i$ is an integer by induction on $n$ using equation (3.4), given that we established at the outset that $y_0$ and $y_1$ are integers. You can recap induction in section 2.5.

## Afterword

The technique involving Fermat's method of descent and switching between roots of a quadratic is called *Vieta jumping*. Solution 2 is not quite classic Vieta jumping, but it is not far off. See 2007 Problem 2 for a classical application of the technique.

The method of solution originally given in the BMO solutions booklet was as follows. Observe that

$$y_{n+1}^2 - 3y_{n+1}y_n + y_n^2 + 1 = 0$$

for all $n \geq 0$. Assume that $n \geq 1$. The preceding instance of the formula is

$$y_n^2 - 3y_n y_{n-1} + y_{n-1}^2 + 1 = 0.$$

Now subtract and factorize, to discover that

$$(y_n - y_{n+1})(y_{n+1} - 3y_n + y_{n-1}) = 0.$$

Therefore $y_{n+1}$ is either $3y_n - y_{n-1}$ or $y_{n-1}$. The latter is not the case but we do not need to dispose of this possibility, because the inductive argument that each term $y_i$ is an integer works perfectly well without doing such housekeeping.

This argument has the merit of being impressive. It seems like mathematical wizardry to take different instances of a formula, subtract them and then factorize. Indeed, this is a dazzling party trick. However, from the point of view of solving problems against the clock, polished technique usually wins out against the search for magic.

# Problem 4

Suppose that $B_1, B_2, \ldots, B_n$ are $n$ spheres of unit radius arranged in such a way that each sphere touches exactly two others externally. Let $P$ be a point outside all these spheres, and let the $n$ points of contact be $C_1, C_2, \ldots, C_n$. The length of the tangent from $P$ to the sphere $B_i$ $(1 \leq i \leq n)$ is denoted $t_i$.

Prove that the product of the quantities $t_i$ is not more than the product of the distances $PC_i$.

*[Geoff Smith, University of Bath]*

## Discussion

This was the first question I posed to appear in a mathematics competition. It will help if you know the theorem of Apollonius concerning the length of a median of a triangle in terms of its side lengths.

To elaborate, we suppose that triangle $ABC$ (figure 3.4) has sides of length $a, b$ and $c$ in the usual positions.

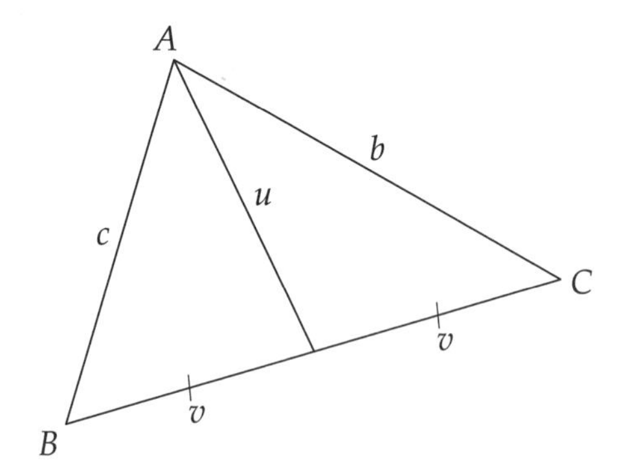


*Figure 3.4*

Let $u$ be the length of the median joining $A$ to the midpoint of $BC$ and let $v = \frac{1}{2}a$. The result is that

$$b^2 + c^2 = 2u^2 + 2v^2.$$

There are various ways to see why this is true. For example, we may consider triangle $ABC$ as being half of parallelogram $ABXC$ in figure 3.5.

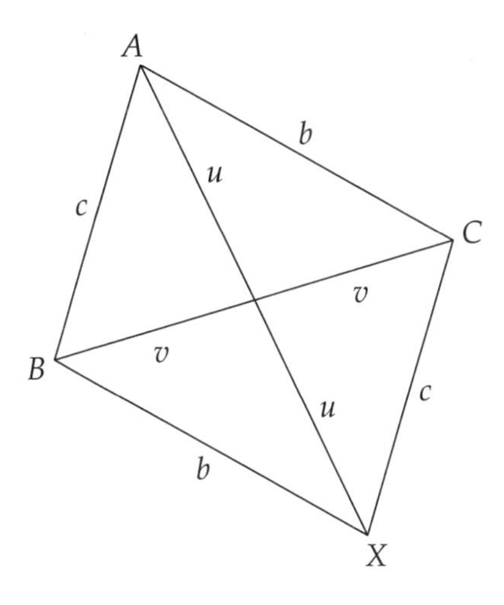


*Figure 3.5*

We cut the parallelogram along the diagonal $BC$ and discard one of the two pieces. As everyone should know, the sum of the squares of the diagonals of a parallelogram is the sum of the squares of each of its four sides. That does it.

This theorem of Apollonius is a special case of of Stewart's theorem. While we are at it, we may as well elaborate on Stewart's theorem. This time suppose that triangle $ABC$ is drawn anticlockwise, and that a point $D$ on $BC$ is such that $BP = m$ and $PC = n$ (so everything is alphabetically memorable). Let the median $AD$ have length $d$. Then

$$amn + ad^2 = mb^2 + nc^2.$$

In the event that you have difficulty remembering this formula, there is a widely used unsavoury and insensitive mnemonic: $man + dad = bmb + cnc$, and you remember "a man and his dad put a bomb in the sink". The reader is invited to invent their own more appropriate mnemonic, to help them to remember figure 3.6 on the next page and Stewart's theorem. If you invent a good one, please let me know for future editions of this text.

Now let us focus on the problem. There was a time when three-dimensional geometry problems appeared frequently in mathematics competitions, but over the years this topic has become quite rare. When studying the interaction between a pair of spheres in contact, we have the

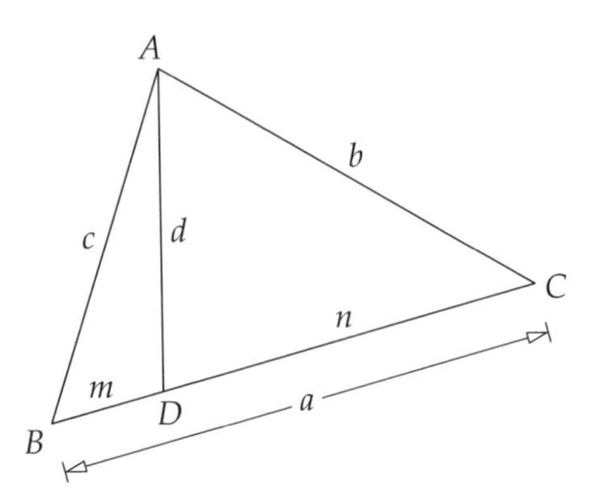


*Figure 3.6*

option of considering the intersection of these spheres with a plane which passes through both $P$ and the centres of both spheres, and we may work with lines through $P$ which are tangent to these spheres which happen to lie in this plane. Notice that the contact point $C$ of these spheres is on a line through their centres, and so lies in this plane. In this way, at least locally, the problem becomes one of plane geometry, and the configuration is shown in figure 3.7. It is possible that $P$ lies on the line of centres of the two circles, but in fact this causes no complications.

## Solution

The spheres all have radius 1. Suppose that spheres $B_l$ and $B_m$ are in contact at a point $C_k$, and that these spheres have centres $O_l$ and $O_m$ respectively. The points of contact are $C_1, C_2, \ldots, C_n$. By the theorem of Pythagoras $PO_l^2 = 1 + t_l^2$ and $PO_m^2 = 1 + t_m^2$, so $PO_l^2 + PO_m^2 = t_l^2 + t_m^2 + 2$.

Applying the theorem of Apollonius to triangle $PO_mO_l$, we obtain $PO_l^2 + PO_m^2 = 2PC_k^2 + 2$, as illustrated in figure 3.7. This robust theorem still holds in the degenerate situation that $P$ lies on the line $O_lO_m$.

Therefore $PC_k^2 = \frac{1}{2}\left(t_l^2 + t_m^2\right) \geq t_l t_m$. We justify this by deploying the AM-GM inequality or by noticing that $\left(t_l - t_m\right)^2 \geq 0$.

Each sphere has two points of contact with other spheres, and so each symbol $t_i$ occurs twice in an inequality of the form $PC_k^2 \geq t_l t_m$, so when

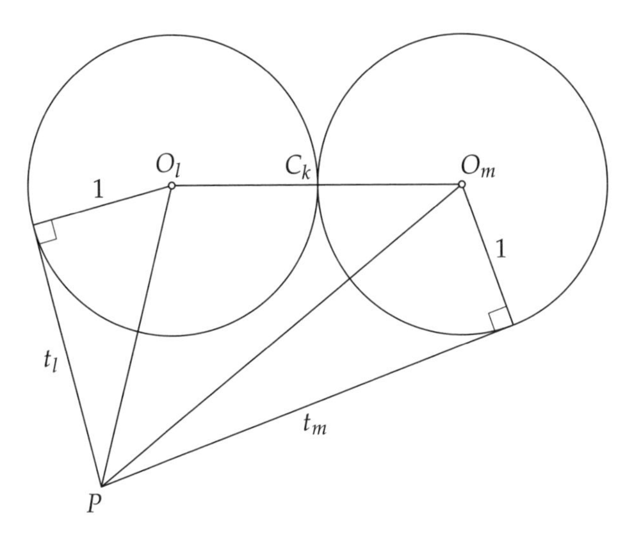


*Figure 3.7*

we multiply over all contact points and extract square roots, we obtain

$$\prod_{i=1}^{n} PC_i \geq \prod_{i=1}^{n} t_i.$$

## Afterword

It is always interesting to determine when an inequality becomes an equality. In our case this happens precisely when $(t_l - t_m)^2 = 0$ for all touching spheres, and so when the spheres mentioned in the problem all have their centres on a sphere with centre $P$.

# 2003 solutions

## Problem 1

For each integer $n > 1$, let $p(n)$ denote the largest prime factor of $n$. Determine all triples of distinct positive integers satisfying

(i) $x, y, z$ are in arithmetic progression and

(ii) $p(xyz) \leq 3$.

*[Adrian Sanders, Trinity College, Cambridge]*

### Discussion

It is sufficient to understand those triples $x$, $y$ and $z$ with the property that their greatest common divisor is 1. Why is this? Note that some people use the term highest common factor instead of greatest common divisor. The two expressions mean exactly the same thing.

The word distinct is used to mean that $x, y$ and $z$ are different from one another. In many circumstances, the word "distinct" can usefully be replaced by the word "different", and this author would like dramatically to curtail the pointless use of "distinct" in mathematics.

### Solution

If the positive integer $d$ is a common divisor of $x$, $y$ and $z$ satisfying the condition, we may divide through by $d$ and obtain another solution because if $x$, $y$ and $z$ are different, then so too are $\frac{x}{d}, \frac{y}{d}$ and $\frac{z}{d}$. Alternatively, we may take any triple $x$, $y$ and $z$ satisfying the conditions of the problem, and obtain another by multiplying each quantity by the same positive integer provided that it is divisible by no prime bigger than 3. It therefore suffices to understand those $x$, $y$ and $z$ which satisfy the conditions, and are such that the greatest common divisor of these three numbers is 1.

The three numbers $x$, $y$ and $z$ are different, so this arithmetic progression is not constant. By exchanging $x$ and $z$ if necessary, we may assume that $x < y < z$. Any common factor of $y$ with either $x$ or $z$ is a divisor of the other because $2y = x + z$, and it follows that $\gcd(x, y) = \gcd(y, z) = 1$. If $y$ were a multiple of 6, then it would have a non-trivial common factor with $z$ by condition (ii), and this is not the case. Thus either (a) $y$ is a power of 2, and both $x$ and $z$ are powers of 3, or (b) $y$ is a power of 3, and both $x$ and $z$ are powers of 2. We separate these cases.

**Case (a)**

There is no solution with $x < y = 1$. Thus we may assume that $y = 2^a$ with $a \geq 1$ and $z = 3^b$ with $b \geq 1$. Now $2^{a+1} = 1 + 3^b$. Working modulo 3 we find that $a + 1 = 2m$ is even. Therefore $3^b = (2^m - 1)(2^m + 1)$. The only powers of 3 which differ by 2 are 1 and 3, so $b = 1$ and indeed $(x, y, z) = (1, 2, 3)$ is a solution.

**Case (b)**

Suppose that $x = 1$. Now $z > 1$ is a power of 2, so $2y = x + z$ is a parity violation. Therefore $x = 2^a$ and $z = 2^c$ with $1 \leq a < c$. Now $2y = x + z = 2^a + 2^c$ is impossible if $a \geq 2$ because the right-hand side is divisible by 4 but the left-hand-side is not. Therefore $x = 2, y = 3^b$ and $z = 2^c$. One can spot the valid solution $(x, y, z) = (2, 3, 4)$. There is no solution with $c = 3$, so it remains to consider the case that $2 + 2^c = 2 \times 3^b$ where $c \geq 4$. In this event $1 + 2^{c-1} = 3^b$. Working modulo 8 it follows that $b = 2n$ is even. Then $2^{c-1} = (3^n - 1)(3^n + 1)$. Now these last two factors differ by 2, and the only way that they can both be powers of 2 is if $n = 1$. This gives rise to the valid solution $(x, y, z) = (2, 9, 16)$.

Now, the list of all possible solutions $(x, y, z)$ is obtained by multiplying through by a positive integer corresponding to the gcd which was divided out earlier. The solutions are therefore $(d, 2d, 3d)$, $(2d, 3d, 4d)$ and $(2d, 9d, 16d)$ as $d$ ranges over the positive integers involving only 2s and 3s in their prime factorizations, together with the solutions obtained by reversing these triples.

## Afterword

There was once a famous unproved result called the Catalan conjecture. This stated that the only two proper powers of integers which differ by 1 are 8 and 9. By *proper power* we mean an $m$-th power where $m \geq 2$. This unproved result no longer exists, because in 2002 it was proved by Preda Mihăilescu, and so it has the status of a theorem. Some of the arguments in the solution above may be simplified by quoting Mihăilescu's theorem. It is well worth noting any new results in elementary mathematics which are discovered, just in case you can deploy them to solve an olympiad problem. Now, in a sense this is not entirely honourable unless you understand the proof of the result, but quoting theorems is not against the rules. If you know them, use them, and win yourself more time to work on the other problems.

I once submitted a problem to the British Mathematical Olympiad setting committee which included Fermat's last theorem (really Wiles's theorem) as an ingredient in the solution. This offering was scornfully rejected, and on reflection I agree. You should not design a mathematics competition to be a test of knowledge. It should be a test of ingenuity, but of course there will always be advanced theorems to which people appeal. Somehow it is more acceptable if the proofs of the theorems are within the range of the contestants. Fermat's last theorem is not in that category.

# Problem 2

Let $ABC$ be a triangle, and let $D$ be a point on $AB$ such that $4AD = AB$. The half-line $l$ is drawn on the same side of $AB$ as $C$, starting from $D$ and making an angle of $\theta$ with $DA$ where $\theta = \angle ACB$.

If the circumcircle of $ABC$ meets the half-line $l$ at $P$, show that $PB = 2PD$.

*[Alan West, University of Leeds]*

## Discussion

This was set as a BMO2 problem, but really it would not sit well in this category today. It is a nice exercise of course, but would now belong on a BMO1 paper, and near the beginning. Back in 2003 the support apparatus now provided for young maths olympians in the UK was still very much under development, and in those days BMO marking was a depressing experience. Huge numbers of students would score very poorly at BMO1, and even though BMO2 is far more selective, it faced similar difficulties. Perhaps this extremely accessible question was set in order to give encouragement. The publications, mentoring schemes, competitions and efforts of teachers to incorporate proper geometry problems into secondary school teaching have made a serious dent in this problem. It is chilling to remember where we were before this huge collective effort was made.

I would prefer to rename $\angle ACB$ as $\angle BCA$ in line with consistent labelling conventions, but the original wording was as above.

## Solution

The only role of $C$ is to define the circle. Notice that $\angle BPA = \angle BCA$ by angles in the same segment. The point $C$ plays no further part in the game. We have figure 4.1 in which the superfluous point $C$ has been suppressed.

There are now various ways to proceed. We can consider areas or deploy trigonometry, but these are surely not the simplest methods.

Triangles $PAD$ and $BAP$ are similar because $\angle PAD = \angle PAB$ is common to both triangles, and it is given that $\angle ADP = \angle BPA$. Two angles match, and therefore so does the third, so these triangles are (indirectly) similar.

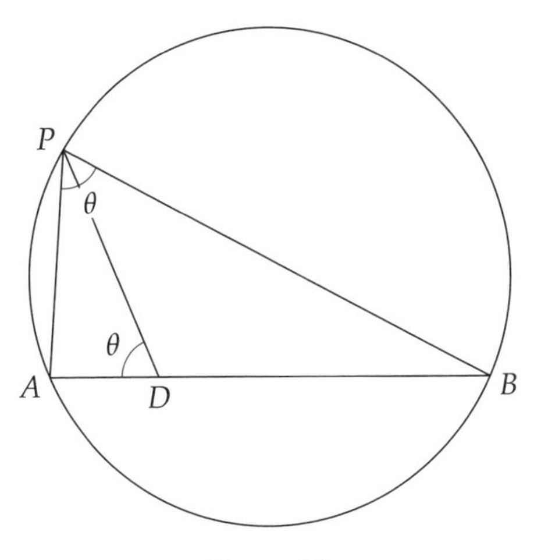


*Figure 4.1*

We have a similarity $PAD \sim BAP$ and the question asks us about the ratio of the lengths $PB$ and $PD$. Reading off the similarity information we have

$$\frac{PA}{BA} = \frac{AD}{AP} = \frac{DP}{PB}.$$

Now is the time to discard concerns about signed lengths, and to stop worrying that the line segments in the numerators are from an anticlockwise triangle but those in the denominator are from a clockwise triangle. This allows us to play fast and loose with the order of letters, and deem that the lengths of the line segments $DP$ and $PD$ are the same.

Therefore $AP^2 = AD \times AB = 4AD^2$. This 4 has just entered the game because the question states that $AB = 4AD$. Therefore $\frac{AP}{AD} = 2$ and so $\frac{PB}{PD} = 2$ as required.

## Afterword

There are, of course, other ways to proceed, for example by comparing areas. Notice that $[ABP] = 4[ABP]$.

Note that I was in mild turmoil as to how to describe the angle $\angle BPA$. Triangle $BAP$ is being described clockwise because of the indirect similarity, so you might think that its angle at $P$ is $\angle APB$, but this seems to violate our "drive in, then turn left" way of describing angles.

In fact, if we are going to be systematic and ideological about this, the angles of a triangle described clockwise should be regarded as negative. Their sum is $-180°$ but working modulo $180°$ this is the same as $180°$, and indeed is $0°$. Once you understand this, you might decide to become a directed angles modulo $180°$ zealot, then you can describe the internal angle of triangle $APB$ at $P$ as $\angle APB$, and feel relaxed that $\angle BPA + \angle APB = 360°$ so $\angle APB = -\angle BPA + 360°$ and this is $-\angle BPA$ modulo $180°$.

# Problem 3

Let $f\colon \mathbb{N} \to \mathbb{N}$ be a permutation of the set $\mathbb{N}$ of positive integers.

(a) Show that there is an arithmetic progression of positive integers $a$, $a+d$, $a+2d$, where $d > 0$, such that

$$f(a) < f(a+d) < f(a+2d).$$

(b) Must there be an arithmetic progression $a$, $a+d$, $\ldots$, $a+2003d$, where $d > 0$, such that

$$f(a) < f(a+d) < f(a+2d) < \cdots < f(a+2003d)?$$

*[A permutation of $\mathbb{N}$ is a one-to-one function whose image is the whole of $\mathbb{N}$; that is, a function $f$ from $\mathbb{N}$ to $\mathbb{N}$ such that, for all $m \in \mathbb{N}$ there exists a unique $n \in \mathbb{N}$ such that $f(n) = m$.]*

*[Ben Green, Trinity College, Cambridge]*

## Discussion

This is a problem where the idea necessary to solve the second part is not enough. It has to be explained. Do not become a victim of the struggle to explain yourself in standard notation. If necessary, feel free to design your own notation. As long as you explain it clearly, that will be fine.

## Solution

(a) In fact you can choose $a$ to be any positive integer, and then find $d$ which works for that $a$. There are only finitely many positive integers less than $f(a)$. The map $f$ is a permutation, so there is a finite (non-empty) set $S$ of positive integers $s$ such that $f(s) \le f(a)$. Now choose a positive integer $n$ sufficiently large that $a+n > \max S$ (so $a+n$ is larger than every element of $S$). Therefore, for every positive integer $d$ such that $n \le d$, we have $f(a) < f(a+d)$.

Consider the infinite sequence of different terms

$$f(a), f(a+n), f(a+2n), f(a+4n), \ldots, f(a+2^k n), \ldots$$

and the various 3-term arithmetic progressions

$$a, a+2^k n, a+2^{k+1}n.$$

We know that $f(a) < f(a+2^k n)$ for every $k \geq 0$, so if $f(a+2^k n) < f(a+2^{k+1}n)$ for some value of $k$, we have found the required three term arithmetic progression. In fact such a value of $k$ has to exist, otherwise

$$f(a+n), f(a+2n), f(a+4n), \ldots, f(a+2^k n), \ldots$$

would be an infinite strictly decreasing sequence of positive integers, and of course that is impossible.

(b) Suppose that $I$ is a finite list of consecutive integers, with first element $u$ and last element $v$. We can define a function $f_I$ from $I$ to $I$ by $f(u+i) = v-i$ for $0 \leq i \leq v-u$. This function has the effect of reversing the list.

Now if we express the positive integers as an union of such non-overlapping lists $I$, we can define a permutation $f$ of the positive integers as follows: for each positive integer $n$, select the list $J$ which contains $n$, and define $f(n)$ to be $f_J(n)$. Notice that $f$ is a permutation of the integers by construction.

Next we will choose the non-overlapping consecutive lists in such a way that if $a$ and $b$ are positive integers, then it is impossible that $f(a) < f(a+d) < f(a+2d) < f(a+3d)$. We make the unusual but uncontroversial observation that $3 \leq 2003$, so the question posed in part (b) will have a negative answer.

The idea is to have the intervals grow in length very rapidly, and contain three times as many numbers as all the lists previously defined. To be specific, let $I_1 = \{1\}$. The next list $I_2$ contains the next $3 \times |I_1|$ numbers: $I_2 = \{2,3,4\}$. Next $I_3$ contains the next $3 \times |I_1 \cup I_2|$ numbers: $I_3 = \{5,6,\ldots,16\}$ and $I_4$ contains the next $3 \times 16 = 48$ numbers: $I_4 = \{17,27,\ldots,64\}$ and so on.

Suppose that $a$ and $d$ are positive integers such that $f(a) < f(a+d) < f(a+2d)$. These numbers $a, a+d$ and $a+2d$ are in different intervals since numbers in the same interval have their order reversed by $f$. Suppose that $a+2d$ is in interval $I$. The number $d$ is less than the number of elements in all earlier lists (since $a$ and $a+d$ are in the union of earlier lists), so $a+2d$ is in the first third of the elements of $I$, and $a+3d$ is in the first two thirds of the elements of $I$. Since $a+2d$ and $a+3d$ are both in $I$, $f(a+2d) > f(a+3d)$.

## Afterword

We were able to prevent an increasing arithmetical progression of length 4 from having an increasing image. We were at liberty to design the permutation $f$ as we wished. If you enjoyed this problem, you could extend it by placing restrictions on the types of permutation $f$ in the game. By tying your hands, you may find that this changes the answer, and that 4 is no longer the critical point of failure.

The reader may wish to investigate what happens if we prohibit one of the attributes of the permutation $f$ that we just constructed.

(i) We might only allow bounded permutations $g$. These are permutations $g$ for which there is a positive constant $c$ such that $|g(n)-n| < c$ for all positive integers $n$.

(ii) What happens if you insist that a permutation $h$ consists of a single cycle? This is the situation where if $m$ and $n$ are different positive integers, then either $n$ is in the sequence

$$h(m),\ h\big(h(m)\big),\ h\Big(h\big(h(m)\big)\Big), \ldots$$

or $m$ is in the sequence

$$h(n),\ h\big(h(n)\big),\ h\Big(h\big(h(n)\big)\Big), \ldots$$

This problem was posed by Ben Green, co-author of the celebrated paper "The primes contain arbitrarily long arithmetic progressions" with Terry Tao. The preprint of this result was available in 2004, so Ben Green was clearly thinking hard about arithmetic progressions around then. The paper was eventually published in *Annals of Mathematics* in 2008.

# Problem 4

Let $f$ be a function from the set of non-negative integers into itself such that for all $n \geq 0$

(i) $(f(2n+1))^2 - (f(2n))^2 = 6f(n) + 1$ and

(ii) $f(2n) \geq f(n)$.

How many numbers less than 2003 are there in the image of $f$?

*[Ed Crane, Trinity College, Cambridge]*

## Discussion

Condition (i) looks unusable in its current form, and the temptation to factorize the left-hand side as a difference of squares is very strong.

## Solution

Condition (i) factorizes to give

$$\big(f(2n+1) + f(2n)\big)\big(f(2n+1) - f(2n)\big) = 6f(n) + 1$$

for each $n \geq 0$. It follows that

$$d = f(2n+1) - f(2n)$$

is positive. Note that $d$ may depend on $n$. Condition (ii) does not involve $f(2n+1)$, which we temporarily eliminate from consideration by means of our newly-minted positive integer difference $d$. We have

$$\big(d + 2f(2n)\big)d = 6f(n) + 1. \tag{4.1}$$

Use condition (ii) to see that

$$d^2 + 2df(2n) \leq 6f(2n) + 1$$

for each $n$. If $f(2n) = 0$, then $d = 1$. Otherwise we may assume that $f(2n) \neq 0$, so $d^2 + 2df(2n) \leq 6f(2n) + 1$ and so $d$ is less than 3. However, $d$ is not 2 by parity. Therefore $d = 1$ for every $n \geq 0$. Equation (4.1) yields

$$2f(2n) = 3f(n)$$

for all $n \geq 0$. Therefore $f(0) = 0$ and $f(1) = d + f(0) = 1$.

At this point it is possible to have a flash of insight, to understand exactly what is going on, and to finish the problem in a few seconds. It is worth pausing here, staring at the displayed formulas, and waiting to feel a tap on the intellectual shoulder.

In the absence of a gift from the subconscious, we can always resort to work. Experiment will indicate that the function $f$ may be strictly increasing. For example $f(2) = 3f(1) = 3$, $f(3) = 1 + f(2) = 4$, $f(4) = 3f(2) = 9$, $f(5) = 1 + f(4) = 10$ and $f(6) = 3f(3) = 12$.

It is clear that $f(i) < f(i+1)$ when $i$ is even because $f(i+1) - f(i) = 1$. Suppose that $i$ is odd. Then $i + 1 = 2m$ and $f(i) = 1 + f(i-1)$. Now $f(i+1) - f(i-1) = 3(f(m) - f(m-1)) \geq 3$ since $m < i+1$ and induction applies. Also $f(i) - f(i-1) = 1$ so $f(i) < f(i+1)$. The inductive proof is complete.

Now we perform some experiments to capture 2003 between successive values if $f$. It is particularly easy to evaluate $f$ at powers of 2, and so to check that $f(128) = 3^7 f(1) = 3^7 = 2187 > 2003$. On the other hand

$$\begin{aligned} f(127) &= 3f(63) + 1; \\ f(63) &= 3f(31) + 1; \\ f(31) &= 3f(15) + 1; \\ f(15) &= 3f(7) + 1; \\ f(7) &= 3f(3) + 1 \\ \text{and } f(3) &= 3f(1) + 1 = 4. \end{aligned}$$

Unpacking all that, we discover that the strictly increasing function $f$ has the property that $f(127) = 1093 < 2003 < 2187 = f(128)$. Therefore there are 128 different numbers, $f(0), f(1), \ldots, f(127)$ less than 2003 and in the image of $f$.

## Afterword

The smart way to finish the argument is to look at the formulas

$$f(2n+1) = 3f(n) + 1 \text{ and } 2f(2n) = 3f(n)$$

for every non-negative integer $n$, with $f(0) = 1$ and $f(1) = 1$, and imagine $n$ represented in binary. Notice that $f(n)$ is obtained by interpreting a binary string as a ternary string (that is, work in base 3), then $f(n)$ is the value of that base 3 number.

Thus

$$f(127_{10}) = f(1111111_2) = 1111111_3 = 1093_{10}$$

and

$$f(128_{10}) = f(10000000_2) = 10000000_3 = 2187_{10}.$$

Shazzam!

I was very surprised to discover that Ed Crane was the author of this problem. There is a long and glorious history of David Monk concocting fiendish problems about sequences, usually with a whiff of binary. Problem 2011/3 is a characteristic example of this type. Ed Crane must have been channelling David Monk to create Problem 2003/4.

# 2004 solutions

## Problem 1

Let $ABC$ be an equilateral triangle and $D$ be an internal point of the side $BC$. A circle, tangent to $BC$ at $D$, cuts $AB$ internally at $M$ and $N$, and $AC$ internally at $P$ and $Q$.
Show that $BD + AM + AN = CD + AP + AQ$.

*[Gerry Leversha, St Paul's School]*

### Discussion

The triangle $ABC$ is equilateral, so its angles are all $60°$. The configuration is straightforward, and any attempt to verify this equation by algebraic or trigonometric means has a good chance of success. However, the diagram cries out "power of a point" or equivalently "the tangent-secant theorem". See section 2.2 on page 16. That has to work, and it cannot be very difficult because the configuration is so simple.

### Solution

Let each side of the equilateral have length 1. Why not? Just choose your units that way. Look at figure 5.1 on the following page and use power of a point.

We have

$$\begin{aligned} BD^2 &= BM \times BN \qquad (5.1) \\ &= (1 - AM)(1 - AN) \end{aligned}$$

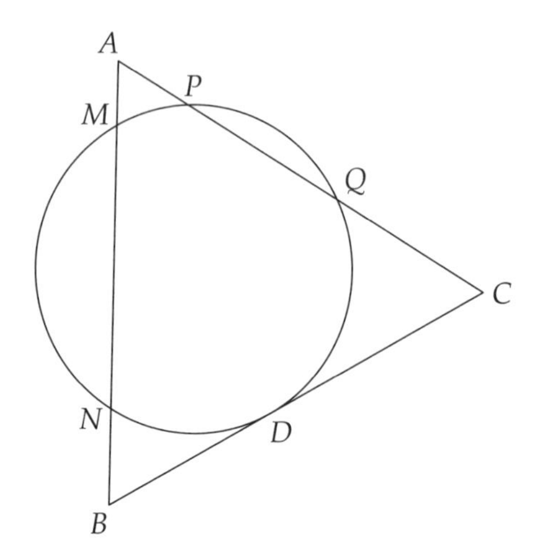


*Figure 5.1*

so that

$$BD^2 = 1 - (AM + AN) + AM \times AN. \tag{5.2}$$

Similarly

$$DC^2 = 1 - (AP + AQ) + AP \times AQ. \tag{5.3}$$

Now again by power of a point (the intersecting chords theorem) $AM \times AN = AP \times AQ$ so the urge to subtract equation (5.3) from equation (5.2) is irresistible. We obtain

$$BD^2 - DC^2 = AP + AQ - AM - AN$$

but

$$BD^2 - DC^2 = (BD + DC)(BD - DC) = BD - DC$$

because $BD + DC = BC = 1$. Therefore

$$BD - DC = AP + AQ - AM - AN$$

which rearranges to $BD + AM + AN = DC + AP + AQ$ as required.

## Afterword

Given a correct understanding of what theorems are most relevant, the problem almost solves itself. The interested reader might like to work with a similar configuration but replace the equilateral triangle by one with sides of length $a$, $b$ and $c$ in the standard positions. An attractive generalization awaits discovery by the inquisitive reader.

One can press on, What formula can be obtained with a general triangle if the circle is not necessarily tangent to the side $BC$, but rather cuts it at $U$ and $V$? The configuration is now symmetric, with no side having special status. Is that expressed in the symmetry of the resulting formula? What happens when there is tangency on all three sides, and the circle is the incircle of triangle $ABC$? What happens if we remove the restriction that the circle cuts the sidelines between each pair of vertices, but rather cuts the lines which extend the sides in a general way? What happens when the circle is an excircle of triangle $ABC$?

# Problem 2

Show that there is an integer $n$ with the following properties:

(i) the binary expansion of $n$ has precisely 2004 0s and 2004 1s;

(ii) 2004 divides $n$.

*[Ben Green, Trinity College, Cambridge]*

## Discussion

There are two fairly natural approaches to this problem. The most straightforward is to observe that if you pop zeros to the right of a binary string, the number being represented is multiplied by a power of 2. Therefore if you can find a multiple of 2004 with binary representation involving exactly 2004 ones, but fewer zeros, then you can pad with extra zeros on the right to get a number of the required form.

Now 2004 in binary is 11111010100 which contains a helpful 7 ones and only four zeros. If 2004 were a multiple of 7, you could solve the problem by concatenating this string with itself a suitable number of times and then pad on the right with zeros, for such a number is the sum of lots of numbers which are all have binary representations of the form 11111010100 followed by many zeros. However, 2004 is not a multiple of 7 so, you need another idea. If I told you that, the problem would be ruined, so please think about that yourself.

Another method of approach is to deploy *Fermat's little theorem* which comes in various flavours. One is this: if $p$ is a prime number, and $k$ is an integer which is not a multiple of $p$, then $p$ divides $k^{p-1} - 1$. If you prefer the language of congruences, the punchline can be expressed as $k^{p-1} \equiv 1 \pmod{p}$. An alert reader may have spotted that 2004 is not a prime number, so FLT does not apply immediately. However, it is possible to express 2004 as a product of prime numbers, and that can be a very helpful thing to do. Another thing to note is that a binary representation of a positive integer is actually code for the unique way that the integer can be written as a sum of different powers of 2. If sitting the exam under real conditions, a well-educated student might well jump in and deploy Fermat's little theorem. In fact this appears to be a very bad idea, because although it can be made to work, and I do not know of a way to solve this problem by using Fermat's little theorem which avoids a grubby scramble as part of the argument. On the other hand, a naive approach which ignores Fermat's little theorem can be made to work without fuss.

## Solution 1

The integer $3 \times 2004$ expressed in binary is 1011101111100 which involves 9 ones and only 4 zeros. Now $2004 = 285 \times 7 + 9$, so concatenate 1011101111100 and 285 copies of 11111010100 and you have a binary number which is both divisible by 2004 and involves exactly 2004 1s in its representation. It also has fewer than 2004 zeros, so pad with zeros on the right until you have a binary string which contains exactly 2004 zeros. That does it.

You might ask why we tried multiplying by 3 (that is, 11 in binary) at the outset. The idea is to find a multiple of 2004 which has a binary representation which involves a number of ones which is not a multiple of 7. In fact we were extremely lucky because we immediately stumbled across a number which involved 9 ones. If we had not done this, and had instead tried $5 \times 2004$ which is 10011100100100 in binary, we would have discovered a multiple of 2004 with 6 ones and 8 zeros in its binary representation. Now you could finish by concatenating well chosen quantities of the two strings 11111010100 and 10011100100100 to get a binary string which involves exactly 2004 ones, but use sufficiently few copies of 10011100100100 so that the resulting string involves more ones than zeros. Then pad on the right with zeros to finish.

## Solution 2

An alternative is to find a positive integer $N$ which is the sum of 2004 different powers of 2 and the largest power of 2 involved is $2^{4007}$ (so its binary representation will be balanced with 2004 zeros and 2004 ones). Thus we are looking for

$$N = 2^{r_1} + 2^{r_2} + \cdots + 2^{r_{2004}}$$

where $4007 = r_1 > r_2 > \cdots > r_{2004} \geq 0$. To arrange for $N$ to be divisible by $2004 = 3 \times 4 \times 167$ we will fix things so that $N$ is divisible by 3, 4 and 167. It is easy to arrange divisibility by 4 by insisting that $r_{2004} \geq 2$. Now $2^n \equiv 1 \pmod 3$ when $n$ is even and $2^n \equiv -1 \pmod 3$ when $n$ is odd. We can arrange for $N$ to be divisible by 3 by ensuring that half of the exponents $r_i$ are even, and half are odd.

Now for the most interesting part, arranging for divisibility by the prime number 167. First note that

$$k = 1 + 2 + 2^2 + \cdots + 2^{165} = 2^{166} - 1$$

is divisible by 167 thanks to Fermat's little theorem, and also by 3 since there are an equal number of even and odd exponents. It is the sum of 166 different powers of 2. Thus a binary number consisting of 166 ones followed by at least two zeros is divisible by 2004. By adding such integers, it follows that a binary number consisting of $12 \times 166$ ones followed by at least two zeros is a multiple of 2004. Now $12 \times 166 = 1992$ so padding our string of 1992 ones with 2016 zeros gives a binary number which represents a multiple of 2004. To finish we need to add a binary string containing exactly 12 ones which represents a multiple of 2004 and is not absurdly long (it has at most 2016 binary digits).

We continue to work with binary representations: 167 in binary is 10100111 which contains 5 ones, 2 corresponding to even exponents and 3 to odd exponents. The binary product $10100111 \times 11$ is not helpful because the ones do not occur nicely distributed, but playing around we find that the binary product $1011 \times 10100111 = 11100101101$ contains 7 ones. Now $5 + 7 = 12$ so try concatenating them: you get

$$1110010110110100111$$

which happily has the same number ones in positions corresponding to even powers of 2 as it does corresponding to odd powers of 2. Pad with two zeros on the right to make the integer with this binary representation divisible by 2004. This binary string has 21 binary digits, and $21 \leq 2016$ so the proof is complete.

## Afterword

The moral of the story is that even if you know a theorem which looks relevant to the problem, it is not necessarily a good idea to use it. The straightforward method, the one which avoids Fermat's little theorem, provokes the question: which positive integers are sums of non-negative multiples of 7 and 9, or of 7 and 6? It turns out that $48 = 3 \times 7 + 3 \times 9$ and every larger integer can be expressed as a sum of non-negative multiples of 7 and 9, and that $30 = 0 \times 7 + 5 \times 6$ and every larger integer can be expressed as a sum of be expressed as a sum of non-negative multiples of

7 and 6. The general result is that if $m$ and $n$ are positive integers which happen to be coprime, then the largest integer which fails to be a sum of non-negative integer multiples of $m$ and $n$ is $mn - m - n$. This result was discovered by Sylvester and is an explicit solution of the Frobenius coin problem when there are only two coins. Information is available on the internet.

Here is a proof. Break the non-negative integers into equivalence classes mod $m$. Let $S = S_0$ denote the set of non-negative integers which are divisible by $m$, and if $u$ is a positive integer, let $S_u = u + S$ be the set of integers of the form $u$ added to a number in $S$. We are interested in the union $T$ of the sets $S_{kn}$ as $k$ ranges over the non-negative integers, and in locating the largest positive integer which is not in $T$. Now $m$ does not divide $n$, so $n + S$ and $S$ are disjoint (that is, they have no element in common). Now consider the $m$ sets $S_0, S_n, S_{2n}, \ldots, S_{(m-1)n}$. The numbers in each of these $m$ sets are in the same congruence class modulo $m$. Numbers in different sets are in different congruence classes modulo $m$ because if $0 \leq i < j < m$ and $in \equiv jn \pmod{m}$, then $m$ divides $(j-i)n$. Now $m$ and $n$ are coprime so $m$ divides $j - i$ and therefore $i = j$. However, this is not the case.

If $k$ is a positive integer, then $k = um + i$ where $u$ is non-negative integer and $0 \leq i < m$. Then $S_{kn} = S_{um+i} \subseteq S_i$ because $S$ consists of multiples of $m$. Therefore, although $T$ is defined as a union of infinitely many sets, it is actually a finite union

$$T = S_0 \cup S_n \cup \cdots \cup S_{(m-1)n}$$

of $m$ pairwise disjoint sets. For $0 \leq t \leq m - 1$, the largest integer which is congruent to $tn \pmod{m}$, but is not in $S_{tn}$ is $tn - m$. The largest integer which is not in the union $T$ of these pairwise disjoint sets is therefore $(m-1)n - m = mn - m - n$. This is therefore the largest positive integer which cannot be expressed as a non-negative linear combination of $m$ and $n$.

For example, when $m$ and $n$ are 2 and 3, this number is 1. When $m$ and $n$ are 3 and 7, then this number is 11.

# Problem 3

(a) Given real numbers $a$, $b$ and $c$ with $a+b+c=0$, prove that $a^3+b^3+c^3>0$ if, and only if, $a^5+b^5+c^5>0$.

(b) Given real numbers $a$, $b$, $c$ and $d$ with $a+b+c+d=0$, prove that $a^3+b^3+c^3+d^3>0$ if, and only if, $a^5+b^5+c^5+d^5>0$.

*[Jerome Watson, Bedford School]*

## Discussion

In fact part (a) is a special case of part (b) obtained by putting $d=0$, so you only need do part (b). However, if the plan to do these questions by dazzling algebra, then some people will find part (a) is in range, but part (b) is not. The reason that part (a) is relatively accessible is because of a standard polynomial factorization which expert maths olympiad contestants will know:

$$x^3+y^3+z^3-3xyz=(x+y+z)(x^2+y^2+z^2-xy-yz-zx).$$

There are clever ways to obtain this factorization, but brute force expansion of the right-hand side certainly works. In the context of part (a) of this problem where $a+b+c=0$, we discover that $a^3+b^3+c^3=3abc$ which is sufficiently incendiary to ignite the algebraic fireworks. The original BMO2 solutions booklet contains many ways to solve this problem, some of which are slightly disgraceful and involving case analysis of the signs of the quantities involved. Such determination is heroic, and in its way impressive, but actually there is a natural way to solve this problem which requires just one very good idea at the start.

## Solution

First some notation. Let $s_i=a^i+b^i+c^i$ for all $i\geq 0$. Thus $s_0=3$, $s_1=0$ and $s_2=a^2+b^2+c^2\geq 0$. The good idea is to find a recurrence formula which, for $i\geq 3$, expresses $s_i$ in terms of various $s_j$ with $j<i$.

First you observe that $a$, $b$ and $c$ are the roots of the polynomial

$$(t-a)(t-b)(t-c)$$

which expands to

$$t^3 - s_1t^2 + (ab + bc + ca)t - abc.$$

Therefore the infinite sequences $(a^i) = 1, a, a^2, \ldots$, $(b^i)$ and $(c^i)$ all satisfy the recurrence

$$x_n = s_1x_{n-1} - (ab + bc + ca)x_{n-2} + abcx_{n-3}$$

for all $n \geq 3$. This recurrence simplifies because $a + b + c = 0$ and

$$0 = (a + b + c)^2 = s_2 + 2(ab + bc + ca)$$

so

$$ab + bc + ca = -\tfrac{1}{2}s_2$$

or, if you prefer,

$$s_2 = -2(ab + bc + ca).$$

The simplified recurrence is

$$x_n = \tfrac{1}{2}s_2x_{n-2} + abcx_{n-3}$$

for all $n \geq 3$.

Now by "linearity" (that is, the form of the recurrence), we can add the sequences $(a^i)$, $(b^i)$ and $(c^i)$ to discover that the sequence $(s_i)$ also satisfies the recurrence. This observation pays rich rewards, and using $s_0 = 3$ and $s_1 = 0$ we see that $s_3 = 3abc$. Well, if you recall the earlier discussion, we already knew that, but at least this is a sensible way to discover this fact that does not rely on remembering a celebrity factorization.

Next look at $s_5$, because the questions asks us to worry about the signs of $s_3$ and $s_5$. We have

$$s_5 = \tfrac{1}{2}s_2s_3 + abcs_2 = \tfrac{1}{2}s_2s_3 + \tfrac{1}{3}s_2s_3 = \tfrac{5}{6}s_2s_3.$$

We need not worry about the possibility that $s_2 = 0$, for that would force $a = b = c = 0$ and so $s_3 = s_5 = 0$. Therefore $s_2 > 0$, and the quantities $s_3$ and $s_5$ have the same sign, as required.

Now, all that was unnecessary, since part (a) will follow from our solution to part (b). However, we did it as a kind of warm up exercise, so that the proof of part (b) will seem very natural.

For part (b), the polynomial at the centre of the proof is

$$(t - a)(t - b)(t - c)(t - d).$$

We revise the definition of $s_i$ to be $a^i + b^i + c^i + d^i$ and the corresponding recurrence becomes

$$\begin{aligned} y_n = s_1 y_{n-1} - (ab + bc + cd + da + ac + bd) y_{n-2} \\ + (abc + bcd + cda + dab) y_{n-3} - abcd y_{n-4} \end{aligned}$$

for all $n \geq 4$. First we had better do something about these dreadful coefficients. Fortunately $s_1 = 0$ so

$$0 = s_1^2 = s_2 + 2(ab + bc + cd + da + ac + bd)$$

and therefore the coefficient of $y_{n-2}$ is $\frac{1}{2}s_2$. Now for the coefficient of $y_{n-3}$:

$$\begin{aligned} 0 &= s_1^3 \\ &= s_3 + 6(abc + bcd + cda + dab) \\ &\qquad + 3(a^2b + a^2c + a^2d + ab^2 + b^2c + b^2d \\ &\qquad\qquad + ac^2 + bc^2 + c^2d + ad^2 + bd^2 + cd^2) \\ &= s_3 - 3s_3 + 6(abc + bcd + cda + dab) + 0 \end{aligned}$$

and so

$$abc + bcd + cda + dab = \tfrac{1}{3}s_3.$$

Our recurrence is therefore

$$y_n = \tfrac{1}{2}s_2 y_{n-2} + \tfrac{1}{3}s_3 y_{n-3} + abcd y_{n-4}.$$

As before, the sequence $(s_i)$ obeys the recurrence, so

$$s_5 = \tfrac{1}{2}s_2 s_3 + \tfrac{1}{3}s_3 s_2 + 0 = \tfrac{5}{6}s_3 s_2$$

and just as before we may neglect the possibility that $s_2 = 0$, so $s_2 > 0$ and the quantities $s_3$ and $s_5$ have the same sign.

## Afterword

Let us see how this works in the absurdly simple situation that there are only two quantities $a$ and $b$, and $a + b = 0$. The polynomial $(t-a)(t-b)$ is $t^2 + ab$ and the associated recurrence is $z_n = -z_{n-2}$. The sequence $s_i$ satisfies this recurrence, $s_0 = 2$, $s_1 = 0$ and $s_i = a^i + b^i$. From this we learn that $s_i = 0$ for odd $i$. In particular, since $s_i = 0$ for odd $i$ when $s_1 = 0$, then by an advanced form of the remainder theorem, $s_1$ should divide each such $s_i$ as a polynomial. Using the same idea again, when the subscript is 3 we learn that $a^3 + b^3$ has $a + b$ as a polynomial factor. In this sense, the factorization

$$x^3 + y^3 + z^3 - 3xyz = (x + y + x)(x^2 + y^2 + z^2 - xy - yz - zx)$$

is the three variable generalization of $x^3 + y^3 = (x + y)(x^2 - xy + y^2)$, and indeed setting $z = 0$ makes it clear.

Other beautiful factorizations fall into our hands. For example, in the four variable case we know that if $w + x + y + z = 0$, then $6s_5 - 5s_2s_3 = 0$, where $s_i = w^i + x^i + y^i + z^i$ and so, without the restriction that $s_1 = 0$, we can predict that $s_1$ is a factor of $6s_5 - 5s_2s_3$ by the fancy version of the remainder theorem. If we put $w = z = 0$, then this is obvious. However, if instead we only set $w = 0$. We learn that $6s_5 - 5s_2s_3$ has $x + y + z$ as a factor, which is far from obvious.

The technique of using a polynomial to construct a recurrence that we have developed here is closely related to the solution that we will give to 2012/4.

# Problem 4

The real number $x$ between 0 and 1 has decimal representation

$$0.a_1a_2a_3a_4\ldots$$

and enjoys the following property: the number of *distinct* blocks of the form

$$a_ka_{k+1}a_{k+2}\ldots a_{k+2003},$$

as $k$ ranges through the positive integers, is less than or equal to 2004. Prove that $x$ is rational.

*[Tony Gardiner, University of Birmingham]*

## Discussion

This is a beautiful problem, and has a local to global character. The local information concerns runs of length 2004 of consecutive digits. The global information is the rationality of the number being represented.

Recall that every rational number has a unique decimal representation, provided that you prohibit such representations from ending in infinitely many 9s. Note that some real numbers have multiple representations unless you make this special rule. Thus

$$\frac{3}{5} = 0.600000\ldots = 0.59999999\ldots$$

and there are various notations in use to describe such patterns. The standard decimal notation for a string of infinitely many zeros is the empty notation. Putting dots over the first and last digits in a repeated string is common, as is putting a line over the repeated string. Therefore

$$\frac{3}{5} = 0.6 = 0.6\dot{0} = 0.6\overline{0} = 0.6\dot{0}00000\dot{0} = 0.6\overline{0000000}$$

and

$$\frac{3}{5} = 0.5\dot{9} = 0.5\dot{9}\dot{9} = 0.5\dot{9}9999\dot{9} = 0.5\overline{9} = 0.5\overline{99} = 0.5\overline{999999}.$$

Notice that you can describe a repeating pattern in different ways:

$$\frac{1}{7} = 0.\overline{142857} = 0.1\overline{428571} = 0.14\overline{285714}.$$

A decimal representation is ultimately periodic (eventually the digits get stuck in a repeating cycle) if, and only if, the real number being represented is a rational number.

Enough of generalities and notation. We now address the problem. Let us replace 2004 by an integer $n$, and try to prove the corresponding result for all positive integers $n$. The result certainly holds when $n = 1$ because if $a_1 = a$, then every digit is $a$ and the number

$$0.aaa\ldots = a \times 0.111\ldots = \frac{a}{9}$$

is rational.

So, the induction begins well. However, to complete it correctly seems to be conceptually difficult, for there were only three correct solutions supplied when the exam actually happened. It is often the case that candidates find conceptual questions far more difficult than technical manipulation problems. Technical fluency can easily be rehearsed, but it seems to be the road less travelled to practise the process of having good ideas. Assiduous users of this text are, I hope, walking that path.

## Solution

We claim that, for any positive integer $n$, if there are at most $n$ different blocks of length $n$, then the number is rational. We have seen how to begin the induction with $n = 1$.

Now we assume that the result holds for $n = m - 1$, and prove that the result holds when $n = m$ (the inductive step). Consider the number $x$ in question. If there are fewer than $n$ different blocks of length $n - 1$, then we could apply the inductive hypothesis in the case $m = n - 1$ and $x$ would be rational.

Therefore we may assume that there are at least $n$ different blocks of length $n - 1$. However, there are at most $n$ blocks of length $n$, and these can have at most $n$ different initial fragments of length $n - 1$. Therefore we may assume that there are exactly $n$ blocks of length $n$ and their initial fragments of length $n - 1$ are all different.

It follows that every block of $n - 1$ digits determines its successor digit. Now, there are only finitely many different candidates for blocks of length $n - 1$ so some block occurs more than once in the decimal expansion. It follows that the sequence of digits following the second occurrence is the same as those following the first occurrence, and so the sequence of digits is periodic following the first occurrence. Thus the decimal representation is eventually periodic, and so represents a rational number.

## Afterword

The number 10 played no role in the argument, so the same result will hold in any number base.

There are rational numbers which have more than $k$ blocks of length $k$. For example

$$1234.56789\overline{12}$$

is rational, but has more than 2 blocks of length 2, and moreover it does not sit between 0 and 1 on the number line. Try to modify the statement of this problem to read:

The real number $x$ has decimal representation

$$\pm b_1 b_2 \dots b_r . a_1 a_2 a_3 a_4 \dots$$

Let $t$ be a positive integer.

Show that this representation of $x$ enjoys the property that *something about blocks of length $t$* if, and only if $x$ is rational.

Ideally you want a statement which has a proof which is close to a solution of this BMO2 problem. Recycling old proofs to obtain better results is a worthwhile game.

# 2005 solutions

## Problem 1

The integer $N$ is positive. There are exactly 2005 ordered pairs $(x,y)$ of positive integers satisfying

$$\frac{1}{x}+\frac{1}{y}=\frac{1}{N}.$$

Prove that $N$ is a perfect square.

*[Jerome Watson, Bedford School]*

### Discussion

There is a well known result that the number of positive integers which divide a positive integer $N$ is odd exactly when $N$ is a square. There is a rather routine way to show this by using the Fundamental Theorem of Arithmetic. You factorize $N$ into a product of powers of different prime numbers:

$$N = p_1^{u_1} p_2^{u_2} \cdots p_k^{u_k}$$

and then observe that the positive integers which divide this number are those of the form

$$p_1^{v_1} p_2^{v_2} \cdots p_k^{v_k}$$

where, for each $i$, we have $0 \le v_i \le u_i$. There are

$$(u_1+1)(u_2+1)\cdots(u_k+1)$$

ways of choosing the list of exponents, and each choice gives rise to a different factor of $N$. Therefore the number of positive integer divisors of

$N$ is odd if every $u_i$ is even, and otherwise it is even. In other words, the number of positive integer divisors of $N$ is odd if $N$ is a (perfect) square, and otherwise it is even.

The technique just described is worth knowing, but as sometimes happens, there is a very slick way to obtain the same result. The positive integer factors of $N$ come in pairs of different factors $d$ and $d'$ such that $dd' = N$, except in the case that $N = k^2$, in which case this method pairs $k$ with itself. Thus there are an even number of factors unless $N = k^2$ is a square, in which case there are an odd number of factors.

This discussion involves ideas which are relevant to the problem under scrutiny. If you make some progress, you are likely to become concerned about the number of positive integer factors of $N^2$ rather than the number of positive integer factors of $N$.

## Solution

This is a problem about whole numbers, so recasting it to avoid the fractions looks to be an attractive first move. The condition given is equivalent to $xy = N(x+y)$. Now you need an idea to proceed. Put everything on the left-hand side, and then add a quantity to both sides so that the left-hand side factorizes. Our condition is equivalent to

$$xy - N(x+y) + N^2 = N^2$$

or equivalently

$$(x-N)(y-N) = N^2.$$

Notice that any solution has $x, y > N$ since the product $(x-N)(y-N)$ is positive, and therefore if one of the positive integers $x$ and $y$ is less then $N$, then they both have that property, so $(x-N)(y-N) = (N-x)(N-y) < N^2$ which is absurd.

Suppose that the prime factorization of $N$ is

$$N = p_1^{m_1} p_2^{m_2} \cdots p_k^{m_k}.$$

The number of ordered pairs $(x,y)$ of positive integers which satisfy this condition is therefore the number of ordered pairs $(u,v)$ of positive integers such that $uv = N^2$, in other words, it is the number of positive integer divisors of $N^2 = p_1^{2m_1} p_2^{2m_2} \cdots p_k^{2m_k}$ and this is $(2m_1+1)(2m_2+$

$1) \cdots (2m_k + 1)$. Now all factors of $2005 = 5 \times 401$ leave remainder 1 on division by 4, so if

$$(2m_1 + 1)(2m_2 + 1) \cdots (2m_k + 1) = 2005,$$

then each $m_i$ is even and so $N$ is a (perfect) square.

## Afterword

Notice that this problem would work just as well for any year which only has prime factors which leave remainder 1 on division by 4, for then all its positive integer factors will leave remainder 1 on division by 4 (why?). In the case 2005, the value of $N$ is $p^{1002}$ where $p$ is a prime number, or $p^2q^{200}$ where $p$ and $q$ are different prime numbers.

# Problem 2

In triangle $ABC$, $\angle BAC = 120°$. Let the angle bisectors of angles $A$, $B$ and $C$ meet the opposite sides in $D$, $E$ and $F$ respectively.
Prove that the circle on diameter $EF$ passes through $D$.

*[Gerry Leversha, St Paul's School]*

## Discussion

There are several angle bisectors on offer here. At least two things should spring to mind: the angle bisector theorem and the theory of excircles. So, do the usual thing. Draw a very precise diagram using permitted instruments. In the British Mathematical Olympiad, and indeed in the International Mathematical Olympiad, the protractor is a forbidden instrument. We can construct an equilateral triangle using ruler and compasses, so making the 120° angle is easy enough. In this case, an accurate drawing will suggest a helpful conjecture. Knowing what you have to prove is more than half the battle, so you time spent creating the precise diagram will have been very well spent. *Wenn ich nur erst die Sätze habe! Die Beweise werde ich schon finden* (Bernhard Riemann).

The angle bisector theorem states that if $ABC$ is a triangle, and the line $l$ is the internal angle bisector of $\angle CAB$, and $l$ meets $BC$ at $D$, then there is an equality of ratios

$$\frac{BA}{AC} = \frac{BD}{DC}$$

and conversely, if $D$ is on the line segment $BC$ and satisfies this ratio condition, then the line $l$ through $A$ and $D$ is the internal angle bisector of $\angle CAB$. See figure 6.1.

If, instead, $l$ is the external angle bisector of $\angle CAB$, and $l$ meets $BC$ (produced) at $D'$, then there is an equality of ratios

$$\frac{BA}{AC} = \frac{BD'}{D'C}$$

and we are not using directed lengths. See figure 6.2. Again, the natural converse holds.

So, there are lots of triangles with which to play, and lots of ratios can be understood, so the sine rule starts to look attractive. A solution can be found that way. However, there is a beautiful short solution which

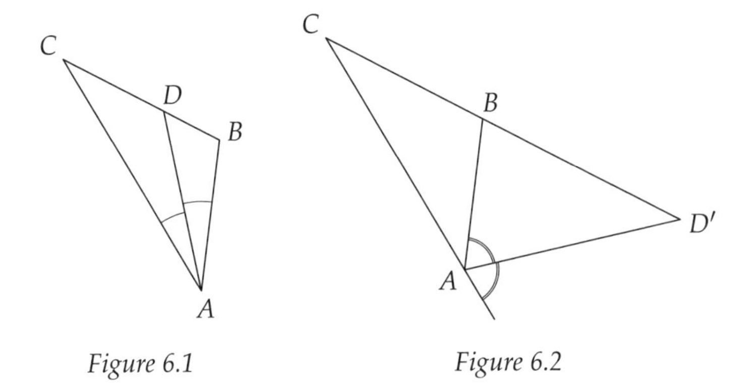


*Figure 6.1* *Figure 6.2*

relies on the theory of excircles (and not that much theory, you just need to know what they are, and how to find their centres).

## Solution

See figure 6.3.

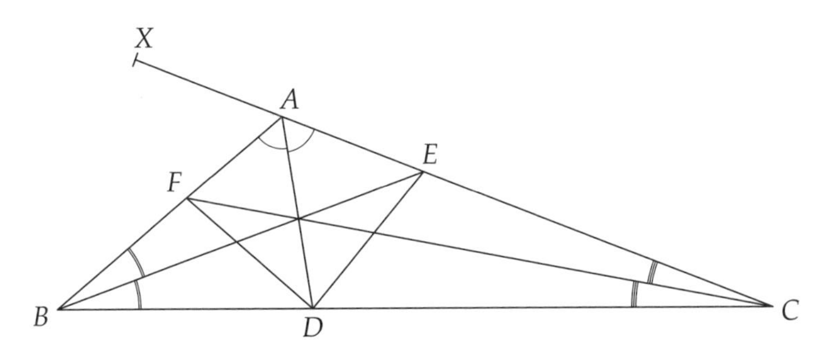


*Figure 6.3*

Put a point $X$ on the ray $CA$ produced beyond $A$. Now $\angle BAX = 180° - 120° = 60°$ and $\angle DAB = \frac{1}{2}\angle CAB = 60°$. Therefore $AB$ is the external angle bisector of $\angle CAD$. The point $F$ is on $AB$ and also on the internal angle bisector of $\angle BCA$. Therefore $F$ is the centre of the excircle opposite $C$ of triangle $CAD$, so $DF$ is the external angle bisector of angle $ADC$. However, $DE$ is the internal angle bisector of this same angle, so $DE$ and $DF$ are perpendicular.

By the converse of angle in a semicircle (Thales), $EF$ is a diameter of the circle $EFD$.

## Afterword

The accurate drawing should persuade you that $FD$ and $ED$ have appropriate bisection properties, from which their perpendicularity follows immediately. These angle bisection properties can then be shown to hold by a variety of methods, including those on display in the solution section.

Perhaps one could have foreseen all this from the outset. After all, the problem quickly reduces to showing that $FD$ and $ED$ are perpendicular. So, how do we show that lines are perpendicular? Well, it might be an angle chase, but it would be disappointing if that was all there was to this problem. It might be that one line is a diameter of a circle, and the other is a tangent line to that circle at an end of the diameter. However, that does not seem likely here because no candidate circle to make this work is apparent, and worse yet, there is a symmetry between the two lines in the configuration which ought to be captured by a good proof. The diagonals of a rhombus, or more generally a kite, are mutually perpendicular. This respects the symmetry of the lines $FD$ and $ED$, but unfortunately no kite is staring back at us when we look at the diagram. Finally, the perpendicularity of internal and external angle bisectors screams out to be used, because the configuration is littered with angle bisectors of various types.

# Problem 3

Let $a$, $b$, $c$ be positive real numbers. Prove that

$$\left(\frac{a}{b}+\frac{b}{c}+\frac{c}{a}\right)^2 \geq (a+b+c)\left(\frac{1}{a}+\frac{1}{b}+\frac{1}{c}\right).$$

*[Adrian Sanders, Trinity College, Cambridge]*

## Discussion

Recall that inequalities are discussed in section 2.1. An interesting feature of the inequality under investigation is that the right-hand side is symmetric but the left-hand side is not. If you exchange $b$ and $c$ but fix $a$, the right hand side stays the same, but the left-hand side becomes

$$\frac{a}{c}+\frac{b}{a}+\frac{c}{b}.$$

This last expression is Banquo's ghost, brooding silently at the feast. There are any number of ways to establish the inequality. Bare hands (sums of squares are non-negative), the AM-GM inequality (see page 14) and the Cauchy-Schwarz inequality (see page 12) can all play useful roles, but hopefully not all in the same proof.

## Solution 1

Let $U = \frac{a}{b}+\frac{b}{c}+\frac{c}{a}$ and $V = \frac{a}{c}+\frac{b}{a}+\frac{c}{b}$. The left hand side is $\frac{a^2}{b^2}+\frac{b^2}{c^2}+\frac{c^2}{a^2}+2V$ whereas the right hand side is $U+V+3$. Since $V \geq 3$ by AM-GM, it suffices to show that

$$\frac{a^2}{b^2}+\frac{b^2}{c^2}+\frac{c^2}{a^2} \geq \frac{a}{b}+\frac{b}{c}+\frac{c}{a}.$$

The Cauchy-Schwarz inequality (see page 12) can be brought into play. However, we apply Cauchy-Schwarz to $\left(\frac{a}{b},\frac{b}{c},\frac{c}{a}\right)$ and $(1,1,1)$ to learn that

$$3\left(\frac{a^2}{b^2}+\frac{b^2}{c^2}+\frac{c^2}{a^2}\right) \geq \left(\frac{a}{b}+\frac{b}{c}+\frac{c}{a}\right)^2 \geq 3\left(\frac{a}{b}+\frac{b}{c}+\frac{c}{a}\right),$$

the final inequality being by AM-GM. Divide by 3 and the proof is complete.

## Solution 2

An alternative cunning proof is to observe that $1 - \frac{a}{b}$ and $\frac{b}{a} - \frac{a}{b}$ have the same sign. Therefore

$$\left(1-\frac{a}{b}\right)\left(\frac{b}{a}-\frac{a}{b}\right)+\left(1-\frac{b}{c}\right)\left(\frac{c}{b}-\frac{b}{c}\right)+\left(1-\frac{c}{a}\right)\left(\frac{a}{c}-\frac{c}{a}\right)\geq 0.$$

If you multiply out and add $\frac{a}{c}+\frac{c}{b}+\frac{b}{a}$ to each side, the problem is solved.

## Solution 3

A third proof in much the same spirit is to observe that

$$\left(\frac{a}{b}-1\right)^2+\left(\frac{b}{c}-1\right)^2+\left(\frac{c}{a}-1\right)^2\geq 0.$$

You multiply out, and then use AM-GM.

## Afterword

Instead of employing the *Cauchy-Schwarz* inequality, one could instead use the *root mean square*, also known as RMS. Recall the chain of inequalities (2.2) on page 15—RMS $\geq$ AM $\geq$ GM $\geq$ HM—which is well worth remembering.

# Problem 4

Let $X = \{A_1, A_2, \ldots, A_n\}$ be a set of distinct 3-element subsets of $\{1, 2, \ldots, 36\}$ such that

(i) $A_i$ and $A_j$ have non-empty intersection for every $i, j$ and

(ii) the intersection of all the elements of $X$ is the empty set.

(a) Show that $n \le 100$.

(b) How many such sets $X$ are there when $n = 100$?

*[Adrian Sanders, Trinity College, Cambridge]*

## Solution

There is no harm in assuming that $A_1 = \{1, 2, 3\}$. The intersection of all these 3-element sets is empty, so among the sets in our collection choose $A_{i_1}$, $A_{i_2}$ and $A_{i_3}$ with 1 not in $A_{i_1}$, 2 not in $A_{i_2}$ and 3 not in $A_{i_3}$. There is the possibility that two of these three sets are equal, and so have the same subscript. They cannot all be equal, for then each of them would have empty intersection with $A_1$.

Suppose that $A_{i_1} = \{a_1, a_2, a_3\}$, $A_{i_2} = \{b_1, b_2, b_3\}$ and $A_{i_3} = \{c_1, c_2, c_3\}$. Every set in our collection $X$ has one of the following doubleton sets as a subset:

$$\begin{aligned}&\{1, a_1\}, \{1, a_2\}, \{1, a_3\},\\ &\qquad\qquad \{2, b_1\}, \{2, b_2\}, \{2, b_3\},\\ &\qquad\qquad\qquad\qquad \{3, c_1\}, \{3, c_2\}, \{3, c_3\}.\end{aligned} \tag{6.1}$$

Notice that it is not necessarily the case that the nine doubleton sets in list 6.1 are all different. We will proceed by showing that at least three different sets in list 6.1 are subsets of at least four sets in $X$, and then exploiting that situation.

Suppose that at most two different sets in list 6.1 are subsets of four or more sets in $X$. Every set in $X$ contains at least one set in list 6.1, so the total number of sets in $X$ is at most $34 \times 2 + 7 \times 3 = 89 < 100 = |X|$. Therefore there are at least three different sets $P_1$, $P_2$ and $P_3$ in list 6.1 which are subsets of at least four sets in $X$.

Now, as promised, we turn our hand to exploiting this situation. Suppose that

$$P_1 = \{a, b\}, P_2 = \{c, d\} \text{ and } P_3 = \{e, f\}.$$

Now $P_1$ is a subset of at least four different sets in $X$, and every set in $X$ has non-empty intersection with each of these four sets. It follows that every set in $X$ contains $a$ or $b$. Similar statements apply to $P_2$ and $P_3$.

Next we show that each pair among $P_1, P_2, P_3$ have an element in common. Suppose, for example, that $P_1 \cap P_2$ is equal to $\varnothing$ (the empty set). Because $P_1$ is contained in sets in $X$ of the form $\{a, b, x\}$ for at least four choices of $x$, and similarly $P_2$ is contained in sets in $X$ of the form $\{c, d, y\}$. Sets in $X$ have three elements, so it follows that in all cases $a \neq x \neq b$ and $c \neq y \neq d$. There is enough flexibility to choose particular values of $x$ and $y$ so that $x$ is neither $c, d$ nor $y$, and $y$ is neither $a, b$ nor $x$. Now $\{a, b, x\}$ and $\{c, d, y\}$ are in $X$ and have empty intersection. This is absurd and so $P_1$ and $P_2$ do not have empty intersection. The same applies to $P_1$ and $P_3$, and to $P_2$ and $P_3$.

We now consider two possibilities, based on whether $P_1 \cap P_2 \cap P_3$ is empty or not.

**$P_1 \cap P_2 \cap P_3 \neq \varnothing$**

Then $P_1 = \{w, x\}$, $P_2 = \{w, y\}$ and $P_3 = \{w, z\}$ because each pair of different sets $P_i$ has an element in common. Recall that every set in $X$ contains at least one of the elements of $P_1$, of $P_2$, and of $P_3$. Therefore if a set in $X$ does not contain $w$, then it is $\{x, y, z\}$.

In this situation $X$ is a subset of the following collection of sets of size 3: the set $\{x, y, z\}$, and all the 3-element subsets of $\{1, 2, \ldots, 36\}$ which contain $w$ and at least one of $x$, $y$ and $z$. The collection we have described is a list of $1 + 3 \times 33 = 100$ sets, and given that $|X| = 100$, the collection we have described is $X$. There are $33 \times \binom{36}{3}$ ways to populate this configuration with particular $w$, $x$, $y$ and $z$.

**$P_1 \cap P_2 \cap P_3 = \varnothing$**

Since the intersection of any two of these three sets is not empty, we have $P_1 = \{x, y\}$, $P_2 = \{y, z\}$ and $P_3 = \{z, x\}$ for different integers in $\{1, 2, \ldots, 36\}$. The set $X$ is a subset of the collection of all 3-element subsets of $\{1, 2, \ldots, 36\}$ which contains at least two of $x$, $y$ and $z$. This is a collection of 100 sets, and so is $X$. There are $\binom{36}{3}$ such collections $X$, and they are different from those described in part (i). Therefore $n \leq 100$, and there are $34 \times \binom{36}{3}$ possible sets $X$.

# 2006 solutions

## Problem 1

Find the minimum possible value of $x^2 + y^2$ given that $x$ and $y$ are real numbers satisfying

$$xy(x^2 - y^2) = x^2 + y^2 \text{ and } x \neq 0.$$

*[Julian Gilbey, Westfield Community Technology College, Watford]*

### Discussion

The problem is posed algebraically, but the geometric significance of $x^2 + y^2$ will not have escaped the alert reader. We give two solutions, the second of which is purely algebraic. However, this problem is slightly unusual for a mathematical olympiad problem because perhaps the most natural approach is to employ trigonometric methods, for example as in our first solution.

### Solution 1

Let the point $(x, y) \neq (0, 0)$ have polar coordinates $(R, \theta)$, so $x = R\cos\theta$ and $y = R\sin\theta$ with $-\pi < \theta \leq \pi$, $R > 0$ and $\theta \neq \pm\frac{1}{2}\pi$. The given equality is equivalent to

$$R^2 \sin\theta\cos\theta(\cos^2\theta - \sin^2\theta) = 1$$

or rather

$$R^2 \sin 2\theta \cos 2\theta = 2,$$

or better yet

$$\sin 4\theta = \frac{4}{R^2}.$$

Now $R^2 = x^2 + y^2$ is at least 4 since $|\sin\psi| \leq 1$ for all $\psi$ and this arises when $\theta = \frac{1}{8}\pi$ and $R = 2$ for example.

## Solution 2

The condition, when squared, is

$$x^2y^2\left[\left(x^2+y^2\right)^2 - 4x^2y^2\right] = \left(x^2+y^2\right)^2. \tag{7.1}$$

Let $p = x^2y^2$ and $s = x^2 + y^2$, so equation (7.1) becomes $4p(s^2 - 4p) = 4s^2$. Now finish by using AM-GM (see page 14):

$$4s^2 = 4p(s^2 - p) = \left(\sqrt{4p(s^2-4p)}\right)^2 \leq \left(\frac{s^2}{2}\right)^2$$

so $s^2 = \left(x^2+y^2\right)^2 \geq 2$ and therefore $x^2 + y^2 \geq 4$. This is achieved when $s^2 = 8p$, so when $x^4 + 2x^2y^2 + y^4 = 8x^2y^2$. To verify that this is achieved, let $y = \lambda x$, so $x^4 + 2x^2y^2 + y^4 = 8x^2y^2$ if, and only if, $x^4(1 + 2\lambda^2 + \lambda^4) = 8x^4\lambda^2$. Since $x \neq 0$, this is achieved by letting $\lambda^2$ be a positive root of $t^2 - 6t + 1$. This quadratic has a positive root between 0 and 1 because it takes the value 1 when $t = 0$ and the value $-4$ when $t = 1$.

## Afterword

Solution 1 relies on transforming the algebra into geometry, and then back into trigonometric functions, which are really another form of algebra. In terms of olympiad problems, the more common ruse is to try to solve geometry problems by one of five types of algebra: Cartesian or areal coordinates, trigonometry, complex numbers or vectors.

Solution 2 shows that equality is achieved when the ratio $\frac{y}{x}$ takes a particular value. Interpreted using trigonometric functions this tells us that solutions arise when $\tan\theta$, and hence $\theta$, takes certain values.

# Problem 2

Let $x$ and $y$ be positive integers with no prime factors larger than 5. Find all such $x$ and $y$ which satisfy

$$x^2 - y^2 = 2^k$$

for some non-negative integer $k$.

*[Paul Jefferys, Trinity College, Cambridge]*

## Solution

There are no solutions when $k \leq 1$ by inspection. If $(x, y)$ is a solution, and both $x$ and $y$ are even, we may divide by 4 to obtain another solution. On the other hand, if we have a solution, we can multiply by 4 to obtain another. If $(x, y)$ is a solution, and one of the two integers is odd, then so is the other. Therefore it is sufficient to understand those solutions where both $x$ and $y$ are odd. $(x-y)(x+y) = 2^k$ and so $x + y = 2^m$ and $x - y = 2^n$ where the integers $m$ and $n$ are both at least 1 and $m > n$.

Solving we find that $x = 2^{m-1} + 2^{n-1}$ and $y = 2^{m-1} - 2^{n-1}$. Since $x$ is odd, $n = 1$. Therefore $x = 2^{m-1} + 1$ and $y = 2^{m-1} - 1$. The reasoning is all reversible and these solutions do make $x^2 - y^2$ a power of 2.

It remains to deal with the restriction that neither $x$ nor $y$ has a prime factor larger than 5. Since $x$ and $y$ differ by 2, no odd prime can divide them both.

First we look at the possibility that $x = 3^u$ and $y = 5^v$ for non-negative integers $u$ and $v$. If $m \geq 2$ this is impossible, because $y \equiv 1 \pmod 4$ but $2^{m-1} - 1 \equiv 3 \pmod 4$. Now $m > n \geq 1$ so it remains to consider the case $m = 2$. Then $(x, y) = (3, 1)$ is a solution. There is an associated infinite family of solutions $(3 \times 2^t, 2^t)$ where $t$ ranges over the non-negative integers.

Next we examine the other possibility that $x = 5^u$ and $y = 3^v$ for non-negative integers $u$ and $v$. Now $3^v = 2^{m-1} - 1$ and $m > 1$. The powers of 3 are all 1 or 3 modulo 8. Therefore $m = 2$ or 3. Now look at $x = 2^{m-1} + 1$. If $m = 2$ this is not a power of 5, but if $m = 3$ we obtain $(x, y) = (5, 3)$, and by reversing the reasoning, or observing that $25 - 9 = 2^4$, this is a solution, and we obtain another infinite family of solutions $(5 \times 2^t, 3 \times 2^t)$ for non-negative integers $t$.

## Afterword

The tricky part of that argument was when we suddenly started working modulo 8. If you square an odd number, the resulting integer is always one more than a multiple of 8, a handy fact which you should note.

The Catalan "conjecture", that is to say, Mihăilescu's theorem., will shorten the proof if you are prepared to quote it. This result was explained in the discussion following 2003/1 and concerns the fact that 8 and 9 are the only proper powers which differ by 1. Thus the power of 5 involved as $x$ or $y$ can be at most the first power. Therefore the interesting last part of the solution can mostly be discarded by quoting Mihăilescu's theorem.

# Problem 3

Let $ABC$ be a triangle with $AC > AB$. The point $X$ lies on the side $BA$ extended through $A$, and the point $Y$ lies on the side $CA$ in such a way that $BX = CA$ and $CY = BA$. The line $XY$ meets the perpendicular bisector of side $BC$ at $P$.

Show that

$$\angle BPC + \angle BAC = 180°.$$

*[Matthew Lee, Trinity College, Cambridge]*

## Discussion

This configuration is extremely rich. The difficulty of the problem is that there are so many things one could investigate, but only some avenues lead to a solution. As with all geometry configurations, draw an accurate diagram, draw cheap conclusions, and work from both ends; what needs to be true so that you can prove the result?

Incidentally, the angles are not being described in the way we recommend. Using our conventions, we should rather aspire to show that $\angle CPB + \angle CAB = 180°$. There is also the problem that the configuration changes if we let $\angle CAB$ be acute. There is so much to say about this problem already, without addressing this issue. The interested reader should study that case to see how the arguments need to be adjusted.

## Solution

We focus on the case when $\angle CAB$ is obtuse. See figure 7.1 on the next page.

The condition that $\angle CPB + \angle CAB = 180°$ suggests that a cyclic quadrilateral should be in play. Let the perpendicular bisector of $BC$ meet the circumcircle of $ABC$ at $Q$ on the arc $BC$ which does not contain $A$. Now $BQCA$ is a cyclic quadrilateral and $\angle CAB + \angle BQC = 180°$. To finish it suffices to show that $Q$ is the reflection of $P$ in $BC$. Let $M$ be the midpoint of $BC$, and we seek to show that $PM = MQ$.

We need an inspiration as to how to proceed. If you stare at your very accurate diagram, then there are several things which suggest themselves:

(i) it seems that triangle $AYX$ is isosceles with apex $A$;

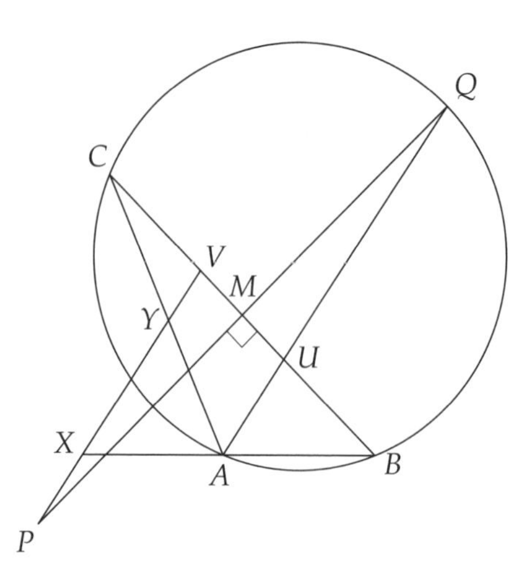


*Figure 7.1*

(ii) it seems likely that the circumcentre of triangle $AYX$ is the intersection of the line $PM$ and the circle $ABC$; and

(iii) it seems possible that the lines $XY$ and $AQ$ are parallel.

All these things are true, and will help you to unlock the problem. Here are three methods which all work, in increasing order of sophistication.

(1) Similar triangles and the angle bisector theorem.

(2) The theorem of Menelaus and the line $XY$.

(3) The Simson line of the centre of the circumcircle of $XAY$.

These ideas inform three solutions.

## Solution 1

We first prove that $XY$ is parallel to $AQ$, the bisector of $\angle CAB$.

Notice that $AX = BX - BA = CA - CY = AY$ so $XAY$ is an isosceles triangle with apex $A$. Its base angles are each equal to half of the exterior angle $\angle CAB$, so $AQ$ is parallel to $XY$.

Now $P$ is on $XY$. Let $XY$ meet $BC$ at $V$ and let $AQ$ meet $CB$ at $U$. Triangles $PMV$ and $QMU$ are similar because corresponding angles are equal. It suffices to show that these triangles are congruent, and we can do that by showing that $M$ is the midpoint of $UV$.

Note that triangles $CAU$ and $CYV$ are similar because $XY$ and $AQ$ are parallel.

Now

$$\frac{BU}{UC} = \frac{BA}{AC}$$

by the angle bisector theorem. Also $BA = CY$, so

$$\frac{BU}{UC} = \frac{BA}{AC} = \frac{YC}{AC} = \frac{VC}{UC}.$$

The final equality is because $CAU$ and $CYV$ are similar. Now $BU = VC$ so the midpoint $M$ of $BC$ is the midpoint of $UV$. The similar triangles $PMV$ and $QMU$ are therefore congruent, so $PM = MQ$ and that finishes the proof.

## Solution 2

When we get to the stage of defining $U$ and $V$ in the previous solution, we could avoid the use of similar triangles by applying the theorem of Menelaus to the collinear points $X, Y$ and $V$. Ignoring signs, we have

$$\frac{AX}{XB} \times \frac{BV}{VC} \times \frac{CY}{YA} = 1.$$

Now $AX = AY$ as observed in proof (i), $XB = AC$ and $CY = BA$ so

$$\frac{BA}{AC} \times \frac{BV}{VC} = 1.$$

Now by the angle bisector theorem

$$\frac{BU}{UC} = \frac{BA}{AC} = \frac{VC}{BV}.$$

Therefore $U$ divides the directed line segment $BC$ in the same way that $V$ divides the directed line segment $BC$, and so the midpoint of $UV$ is $M$, the midpoint of $BC$. We finish in the same manner as in solution 1.

## Solution 3

We begin afresh, starting from the very beginning. We first follow solution 1 so that $AQ$ is parallel to $XY$ and triangle $XAY$ is isosceles with apex $A$.

Note that $BA \times BX = CY \times CA$. This means that each of $B$ and $C$ has the same power with respect to the circumcircle of triangle $XAY$. It follows that $B$ and $C$ have the same distance from the centre $K$ of that circle, so $KP$ is the perpendicular bisector of $BC$.

The centre $K$ of the circle $XAY$ is on the angle bisector of $\angle XAY$. The external angle bisector of this angle meets the circle $ABC$ at $Q$, a point previously discussed, which is also on the line $KP$. The internal and external bisectors of an angle are perpendicular, so $K$ is on circle $ABC$ by the converse of angle in a semicircle (Thales). See figure 7.2.

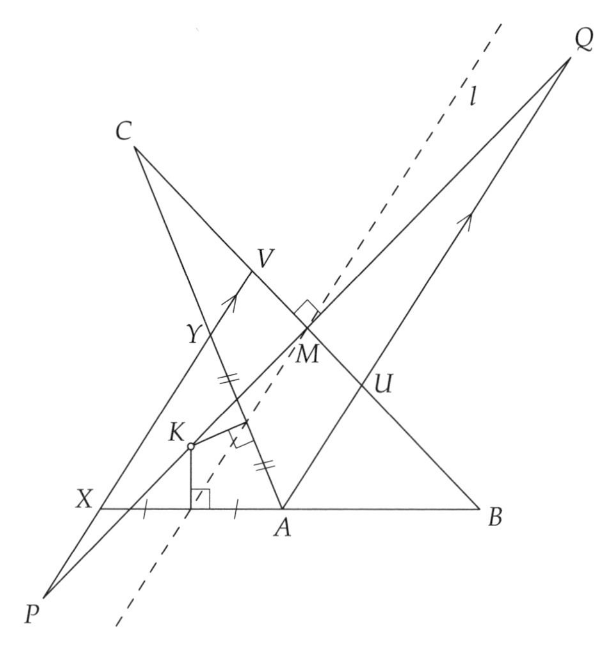


*Figure 7.2*

Now deploy the theory of the Simson line of $K$ on the circumcircle of triangle $ABC$. This Simson line $l$ passes through the feet of the perpendiculars from $K$ to $CA, AB$ and $BC$. The first two feet are the midpoints of $AY$ and $AX$ because $K$ is the centre of the circumcircle of triangle $AYX$, so the line $l$ is the set of points half way between the parallel lines $AQ$ and $PV$. Put another way, the lines $AQ$ and $PV$ are mutual reflections in $l$.

The foot of the perpendicular from $K$ to $BC$ is $M$, and lies on $l$. Enlargement from $M$ with scale factor $-1$ (that is, rotation about $M$ through $180^\circ$) carries $P$ to $Q$, so $M$ is the midpoint of $PQ$ as required.

## Afterword

There is still at least one road not taken. In all three arguments that we have given, we have shown that $P$ reflected in $BC$ lies on the circumcircle of triangle $ABC$. This is a property also enjoyed by the orthocentre $H$ of triangle $ABC$. Therefore it suffices to show that the quadrilateral $PHBC$ is cyclic. In the arguments given so far, $H$ plays only a peripheral role. It is lurking behind the bushes in the theory of the Simson line. In solution 3, $HK$ is bisected by the Simson line $l$ of $K$ with respect to circle $ABC$. It would be very interesting if a reader could solve the problem another way by finding a direct proof of the cyclicity of $PHBC$.

# Problem 4

An exam consisting of six questions is sat by 2006 children. Each question is marked either right or wrong. Any three children have right answers to at least five of the six questions between them.

Let $N$ be the total number of right answers achieved by all the children, that is, (the total number of questions solved by child 1) + (the total solved by child 2) + $\cdots$ + (the total solved by child 2006).

Find the least possible value of $N$.

*[Paul Jefferys, Trinity College, Cambridge]*

## Discussion

You should be able to convince yourself that most students answered the questions quite well, otherwise it is impossible for each group of three children have correct answers to at least five of the six problems between them.

Since you seek a minimum value of $N$, you need to do two things: look for a configuration which gives rise to what you suspect is the least value of $N$, and show that no configuration gives rise to a smaller value of $N$.

## Solution

Notice that $\binom{6}{4} = 15$, so there cannot be 31 or more students who got 4 or fewer questions correct. It follows that at least $2006 - 30 = 1976$ students got at least 5 correct answers. A possible configuration is that 1976 students got exactly 5 questions right, and 30 students got exactly four questions right in such a way that every collection of 4 questions were ones answered correctly by two different groups of 4 students. The value of $N$ for this configuration is

$$1976 \times 5 + 30 \times 4 = 10000.$$

Thus the least possible value of $N$ is at most 10000.

Now we will show that $N$ is at least 10000. Consider the performances of the weakest 30 students. Before we go on, we should settle the objection that one cannot expect the exam performance to discriminate sufficiently well to establish the weakest 30 students, given that we are just measuring the number of correct solutions to only 6 problems. All that you need to overcome this is a way to break ties. For example, you might discriminate between students with the same score by deeming the younger student to be stronger than the older one, since they have had less time to prepare.

If any of the 30 weakest students got perfect results, then for that configuration $N \geq 6 \times 1977 \geq 10000$, so this configuration will not give a better lower bound for $N$. Suppose that $A$ of them got 5 right, $B$ got 4 right, $C$ got 3 right, $D$ got 2 right, $E$ got 1 right and, appropriately, $F$ got 0 right. Therefore

$$A + B + C + D + E + F = 30. \tag{7.2}$$

Suppose that the collective performance of our 30 weakest students is $W$ where

$$W = 5A + 4B + 3C + 2D + E. \tag{7.3}$$

We can modify the configuration by replacing a particular student $X$ who got fewer than four questions right by several new students who did get 4 questions right, including those solved correctly by $X$. The students replacing $X$ all solve different collections of 4 problems. The new configuration will still satisfy the conditions specified in the problem, because any group of students which contains at most one of the new students will collectively solve at least as many as the corresponding group with the new student replaced by the old student, and any group of students which contains at least two of the new students will collectively solve at least 5 problems.

This process may be deployed repeatedly, until every student in the configuration has solved at least 4 problems, including, of course, the weakest 30 students.

As discussed earlier, at most 30 students got no more than 4 questions right. Therefore

$$B + \binom{3}{1}C + \binom{4}{2}D + \binom{5}{3}E + \binom{6}{4}F \leq 30. \tag{7.4}$$

Subtract equation (7.2) from equation (7.4) to obtain

$$-A + 2C + 5D + 9E + 14F \leq 0$$

which can be expressed as

$$2C + 5D + 9E + 14F \leq A.$$

Subtract 4 times equation (7.2) from equation (7.3) to obtain

$$A - C - 2D - 3E - 4F \leq W - 120.$$

This rearranges to

$$A \leq C + 2D + 3E + 4F + W - 120.$$

We conclude that

$$2C + 5D + 9E + 14F \leq A \leq C + 2D + 3E + 4F + W - 120.$$

and so

$$C + 3D + 6E + 10F \leq W - 120$$

and therefore $W \geq 120$ and so

$$N \geq 1976 \times 5 + W \geq 10000.$$

Therefore the least possible value of $N$ is 10000.

## Afterword

Notice that we found an optimal configuration very quickly. Almost all the proof consisted of showing that $N \geq 10000$. We supplied a proper proof. Students might be tempted to take the configuration we mentioned where $N = 10000$ is achieved, and try to argue that one cannot do better than this because if you fiddle with the configuration, the value of $N$ does not decrease. This is a dangerous proof strategy, and often fails.

# 2007 solutions

## Problem 1

Triangle $ABC$ has integer-length sides, and $AC = 2007$. The internal bisector of $\angle BAC$ meets $BC$ at $D$.

Given that $AB = CD$, determine $AB$ and $BC$.

*[Tim Cross, King Edward's School, Birmingham]*

### Discussion

People adhering to the directed angle convention will wince at describing the angle at $A$ in this fashion, when clearly $\angle CAB$ is intended.

### Solution

See figure 8.1.

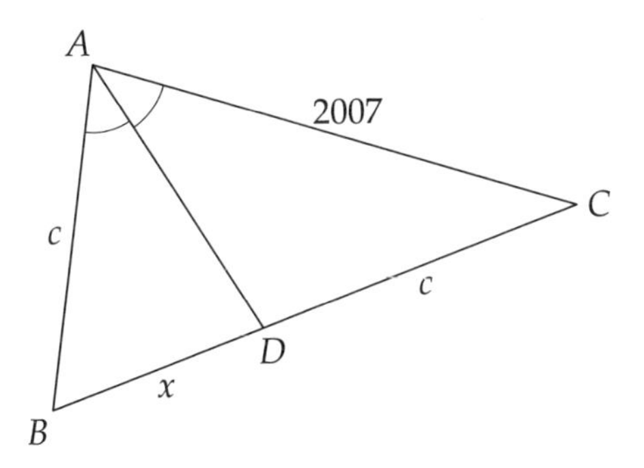


*Figure 8.1*

The standard notation is that the length of $AB$ is $c$. Therefore $DC = c$. It is given that $AC = 2007 = 3^2 \times 223$. Notice that 223 is prime. Let the integer $x$ be the length $BD$. The angle bisector theorem is in play, so $BA : AC = BD : DC$ and we have $\frac{2007}{c} = \frac{c}{x}$ so $c^2 = 9 \times 223x$. Now the Fundamental Theorem of Arithmetic (see page 28) applies, so the integer $x$ is a multiple of 223. In fact $x = 223k^2$ for a positive integer $k$, and $c = 669k$. Now $AB = 669k$, $BC = 223k^2 + 669k = 223k(k+3)$ and $CA = 2007$. We need to identify positive integers $k$ for which these formulas are the side lengths of a triangle. The triangle inequality applies in all three ways (and it is harmless to divide through by the common factor 223).

It is necessary and sufficient that $AB < BC + CA$, $BC < BA + AC$ and $CA < CB + BA$. These conditions are

$$\begin{aligned} 3k &< k(k+3) + 9, \\ k(k+3) &< 3k + 9 \\ \text{and} \quad 9 &< k(k+3) + 3k. \end{aligned}$$

Recall that $k$ is a positive integer. The first condition holds for all $k$. The second holds for $k < 3$ and the third holds when $(k+3)^2 > 18$ and so when $1 < k$. Therefore the only possibility which gives rise to a triangle is $k = 2$, and the triangle has sides $AB = 669k = 1338$, $BC = 223k(k+3) = 2230$ and $CA = 2007$.

## Afterword

That was an amusing fusion question, where you had to start out with geometric arguments, then do some number theory, but then step back into geometry again to use the triangle inequality to finish the argument.

# Problem 2

Show that there are infinitely many pairs of positive integers $(m,n)$ such that

$$\frac{m+1}{n}+\frac{n+1}{m}$$

is a positive integer.

*[Alan West, University of Leeds]*

## Discussion

There is a famous proof technique known as Fermat's method of descent. The idea is that you want to show that a particular number theoretic condition has no positive integer solutions. You suppose, for contradiction, that there is a positive integer which satisfies the condition, and using algebraic cunning, you show that there is a smaller positive integer which satisfies the condition. By applying this argument inductively, you produce an infinite sequence of positive integers where each one is smaller than the last. This is impossible, so the assumption was incorrect, and there can be no positive integer which satisfies the given number theoretic condition.

There are all sorts of variations on this theme. For example, it might be that you want to show that there is no pair of positive integers $(m,n)$ which satisfy a particular condition. Again you might suppose that such a pair exists, and then use mathematics to produce another pair $(m',n')$ of positive integers which also satisfy the condition, and in some sense are a "smaller" solution. For example it might be that $m'+n' < m+n$ or perhaps $\max\{m',n'\} < \max\{m,n\}$ (or other devices). Once again you have a contradiction because there is no infinite descending sequence of positive integers.

In this problem, you are required to find infinitely many pairs $(m,n)$ of positive integers which satisfy a condition. One approach is to reorganize Fermat's method of descent and turn it into a method of ascent. Show that there is a pair of positive integers $(u,v)$ which satisfy the condition, and from that pair manufacture another pair $(u',v')$ of positive integers which also satisfy the condition, and are such that, in some sensible sense, the new pair $(u',v')$ is "larger" than the old pair $(u,v)$. You deduce that there are infinitely many different pairs $(m,n)$ of positive integers which satisfy the condition by an inductive procedure.

## Solution

Consider the condition that

$$\frac{m+1}{n} + \frac{n+1}{m} = k$$

is a positive integer. This is really a quadratic condition, for it is equivalent to the fact that positive integer $m$ is a solution of the quadratic equation

$$x(x+1) + n(n+1) - knx = 0$$

or rather

$$x^2 + (1-kn)x + n(n+1) = 0.$$

Now $m$ is a solution. There is another solution $m'$ where $mm' = n(n+1) > 0$ and $m + m' = kn - 1$, an integer. So $m' = \dfrac{n(n+1)}{m}$ is a positive integer. Suppose now that $m \leq n$, then $m' \geq n+1 > n$. Thus if $(m,n)$ is a solution of our original problem with $m \leq n$, then we have another solution $(n, m')$ with $n < m'$. Measuring the size of a solution $(m,n)$ by $m+n$, we find that we have a way of generating an infinite sequence of different pairs of positive integers $(m,n)$ which satisfy

$$\frac{m+1}{n} + \frac{n+1}{m} = k$$

for some integer $k$

We should not forget to find a single example of a solution to start the ball rolling. Well $(m,n) = (1,1)$ works with $k = 4$. That is it, but for amusement and as a check that this all works, we can write down the first few solutions generated by our method:

$$(1,1), (1,2), (2,6), (6,21), (21,77), \ldots$$

## Afterword

Fermat lived in the first half of the 17th century, so in terms of the history of mathematics, he came just a little before Newton, and indeed their lives overlapped. In the IMO of 1988 in Canberra, the Bulgarian contestant Emanouil Atanassov drove a Fermat-style descent argument by means of the method we have used here. He won an IMO special prize for his solution. Here is the IMO 1988 number theory problem which you can now solve yourself. It requires a few more ideas, but now you know to look at the other root of a quadratic equation, then it may be within range. Atanassov's technique was not completely new, but it was a surprise to the IMO community.

*Let $a$ and $b$ be positive integers such that $ab+1$ divides $a^2+b^2$. Show that*

$$\frac{a^2+b^2}{ab+1}$$

*is the square of an integer.*

So, to summarize: find a solution characterized as a solution of a quadratic equation, and then look at the other root. The advantage of this is that it is a *method*. You can approach the problem by looking for the quadratic polynomial. Without this perspective, you are left to raw ingenuity, and that is hard to produce on demand. In our case, for example, it would consist of noticing that if $(m, n)$ are positive integers satisfying the condition, then so too are $\left(n, \frac{n(n+1)}{m}\right)$. Well, yes, and you can verify that $m$ divides $n(n+1)$ and that the new pair satisfy the condition, but how are you supposed to dream this up? It is all very well if you are Pierre de Fermat, you can make a dozen such observations before breakfast. However, many of us are not Pierre de Fermat, but we can recognize a quadratic equation when we see one.

This method of skipping between roots of quadratic polynomials is widely known as Vieta jumping, following a pioneer in the study of symmetric polynomials Fransiscus Vieta. This is the Latinized form of his real name, which is François Viète (1540-1603).

# Problem 3

Let $ABC$ be an acute-angled triangle with $AB > AC$ and $\angle BAC = 60°$. Denote the circumcentre by $O$ and the orthocentre by $H$ and let $OH$ meet $AB$ at $P$ and $AC$ at $Q$.

Prove that $PO = HQ$.

*[The* circumcentre *of triangle ABC is the centre of the circle which passes through the vertices A, B and C. The* orthocentre *is the point of intersection of the perpendiculars from each vertex to the opposite side.]*

*[Christopher Bradley, ex-Clifton College]*

## Discussion

There are people who really enjoy the techniques of classical Euclidean geometry, where you assemble constructions and theorems to solve the problem. However, a mathematics olympiad is not a beauty contest. If algebraic or trigonometric methods give you free information, then it would be extremely poor tactics not to use that bonus knowledge.

## Solution

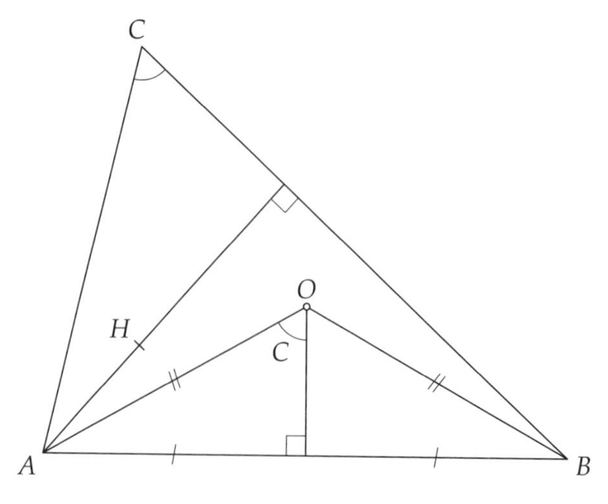


*Figure 8.2*

It is a standard (and quotable) property of the circumcentre and orthocentre of triangle $ABC$ that $\angle OAB = \angle CAH$. See figure 8.2. Another way to say this is that the line $AO$ and the line $AH$ are reflections of one another in the line which is the internal angle bisector at $A$. This is a fact about the reflection of lines, and not a fact about the locations of $O$ and $H$, so one does not expect $O$ to reflect to $H$.

Let the radius of the circumcircle be $R$, so $OA = R$. It is a trigonometric fact that $AH = 2R\cos A$ in any triangle, but in this case $A = 60°$ so $AH = R$. It follows that $O$ and $H$ are mutual reflections in the internal angle bisector of $A$. See figure 8.3. Therefore $OH$ is perpendicular to this internal angle bisector, and so $P$ and $Q$ are reflections of one another in this internal angle bisector, as are the intervals $PO$ and $QH$, which therefore have the same length.

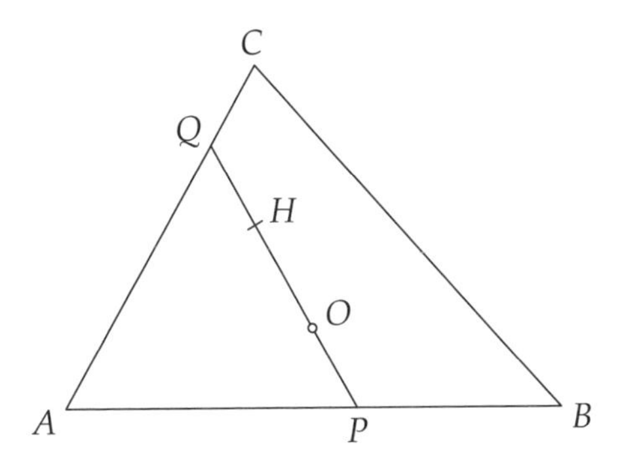


*Figure 8.3*

The proof is complete, but consider how one might solve this problem without noticing the role of the internal angle bisector at $A$. Once you know that triangle $HAO$ is isosceles with apex $A$, then the associated angle fact is that $\angle OHA = \angle AOH$. Taking supplements, we find that $\angle POA = \angle AHQ$. Now, you either have to know, or prove, that $\angle OAB = \angle CAH$ (if you have to discover it, it is an angle chase; both angles are the complement of $\angle C$). Now triangles $POA$ and $QHA$ are (indirectly) congruent using the justification $ASA$.

## Afterword

There is an English idiom, the "elephant in the room", which indicates that there is a major fact which is not being mentioned. Imagine a group of people, politely drinking tea and discussing the weather, carefully avoiding the mention of a prodigious pachyderm. In our case, the elephant is the fact that triangle $QAP$ is equilateral, giving rise to unexpected symmetry.

The importance of symmetry (group theory) in geometry was recognized and developed by Felix Klein (1849–1925). In international mathematics competitions, the marking police are called *coordinators*. They should have agile minds, and be able readily to adapt to different styles of valid proof. Sometimes, however, a coordinator falls short of this ideal. I recall proudly presenting an elegant geometric argument which one of our team had constructed. It was a beautiful piece of reasoning, in the spirit of Felix Klein. The student had taken the original configuration, and added construction lines to make the configuration symmetric, and had finished by exploiting the symmetry. The coordinator objected to this approach because it didn't have congruent triangles in it. Fortunately there is always an appeal procedure.

# Problem 4

In the land of Hexagonia, the six cities are connected by a rail network such that there is a direct rail line connecting each pair of cities. On Sundays, some lines may be closed for repair. The passengers' rail charter stipulates that any city must be accessible by rail from any other (not necessarily directly) at all times.

In how many different ways can some of the lines be closed subject to this condition?

*[Paul Jefferys, Trinity College, Cambridge]*

## Discussion

This could be messy unless you find a systematic way to approach it. In graph theory language, you have six labelled vertices (the cities), and at most one edge joins each pair of different vertices on Sundays. The accessibility condition makes us ask how many such graphs are connected? If we replace 6 by $n$, then an inductive procedure can be put in play.

## Solution

Let the number of connected graphs on $n$ vertices be $f(n)$. Here we do not allow multiple edges between a given pair of vertices, nor do we permit loops, where an edge connects a vertex to itself.

$f(1) = 1$, $f(2) = 1$, $f(3) = 4$. After that one has to think.

Consider a graph with $n$ vertices. There are $\binom{n}{2}$ possible edges, and given that some may be omitted and some not, there are $2^{\binom{n}{2}}$ possible graphs on this collection of vertices.

We will do that calculation again in a way which involves the quantities $f(i)$, and then pop an equals sign between our answers. This strategy is called *double-counting*.

Select and distinguish a vertex $v$ of a particular graph. This vertex lies in a connected component containing $i$ vertices, where $1 \leq i \leq n$. There are $n-1$ other vertices, and $\binom{n-1}{i-1}$ of them can be the other vertices in the connected component of $v$. Given a choice of the other $i-1$ vertices in the connected component of $v$, there are $f(i)$ possible connected components of $v$. The remaining $n-i$ vertices may be connected in any way at all, and that may happen in $2^{\binom{n-i}{2}}$ ways. Therefore

$$2^{\binom{n}{2}} = \sum_{i=1}^{n} \binom{n-1}{i-1} f(i) 2^{\binom{n-i}{2}}.$$

Now

$$\begin{aligned} 64 &= 2^{\binom{4}{2}} \\ &= \binom{3}{0} f(1) 2^{\binom{3}{2}} + \binom{3}{1} f(2) 2^{\binom{2}{2}} + \binom{3}{2} f(3) 2^{\binom{1}{2}} + \binom{3}{3} f(4) 2^{\binom{0}{2}} \\ &= 1 \times 1 \times 8 + 3 \times 1 \times 2 + 3 \times 4 \times 1 + 1 \times f(4) \times 1 \\ &= 26 + f(4) \end{aligned}$$

so $f(4) = 38$. Next

$$\begin{aligned} 1024 &= 2^{10} \\ &= 2^{\binom{5}{2}} \\ &= \binom{4}{0} f(1) 2^{\binom{4}{2}} + 41 f(2) 2^{\binom{3}{2}} + \binom{4}{2} f(3) 2^{\binom{2}{2}} \\ &\qquad + \binom{4}{3} f(4) 2^{\binom{1}{2}} + \binom{4}{4} f(5) 2^{\binom{0}{2}} \\ &= 1 \times f(1) \times 64 + 4 \times f(2) \times 8 + 6 \times f(3) \times 2 \\ &\qquad + 4 \times f(4) \times 1 + 1 \times f(5) \times 1 \end{aligned}$$

so $1028 = 64 + 32 + 48 + 152 + f(5)$, and hence $f(5) = 728$. I hope that you find this relaxing. Off we go again.

> Theirs not to make reply,
> Theirs not to reason why,
> Theirs but to do and die:
> Into the valley of Death,
> Rode the six hundred.
>
> (Alfred, Lord Tennyson)

$$\begin{aligned}
32\,768 &= 2^{15} \\
&= 2^{\binom{6}{2}} \\
&= \binom{5}{0} f(1) 2^{\binom{5}{2}} + \binom{5}{1} f(2) 2^{\binom{4}{2}} + \binom{5}{2} f(3) 2^{\binom{3}{2}} \\
&\qquad + \binom{5}{3} f(4) 2^{\binom{2}{2}} + \binom{5}{4} f(5) 2^{\binom{1}{2}} + \binom{5}{5} f(6) 2^{\binom{0}{2}} \\
&= 1 \times f(1) \times 1024 + 5 \times f(2) \times 64 + 10 \times f(3) \times 8 \\
&\qquad + 10 \times f(4) \times 2 + 5 \times f(5) \times 1 + 1 \times f(6) \times 1
\end{aligned}$$

so $32\,768 = 1024 + 320 + 760 + 3640 + f(6)$, and hence $f(6) = 26\,704$.

The final answer is either 26 704 or 26 703, depending on whether closing no lines at all counts as closing some of the lines. You can be confident that the markers would accept either answer, since both interpretations are reasonable.

## Afterword

On the absence of a direct method, we used an inductive procedure. However, the inductive method did not establish an elegant formula for $f(n)$ for each value of $n$. Instead the inductive process took the form of an algorithm which was possible, with care and determination, to perform by hand.

One could turn the algorithm into code, and thereby construct a computer program which could evaluate $f(n)$ for some values of $n$ which are larger than 6.

# 2008 solutions

## Problem 1

Find the minimum value of $x^2 + y^2 + z^2$, where $x, y, z$ are real numbers such that $x^3 + y^3 + z^3 - 3xyz = 1$.

*[David Monk, ex-University of Edinburgh]*

### Discussion

The expression $x^3 + y^3 + z^3 - 3xyz$ is part of a standard factorization which you should learn. See 2004/3. This factorization is

$$x^3 + y^3 + z^3 - 3xyz = (x + y + z)(x^2 + y^2 + z^2 - xy - yz - zx),$$

a fact which you can verify by simply multiplying out the right-hand side. If you know about $3 \times 3$ determinants, then you will be able to calculate that

$$\begin{vmatrix} x & y & z \\ y & z & x \\ z & x & y \end{vmatrix} = 3xyz - x^3 - y^3 - z^3.$$

Now, this is a very pretty determinant. Let us assume that you know a little determinantal magic, so that if you add the second column to the first and then the third column to the first, then the determinant is unchanged so

$$\begin{vmatrix} x & y & z \\ y & z & x \\ z & x & y \end{vmatrix} = \begin{vmatrix} x+y+z & y & z \\ x+y+z & z & x \\ x+y+z & x & y \end{vmatrix}$$

$$= (x+y+z)\begin{vmatrix} 1 & y & z \\ 1 & z & x \\ 1 & x & y \end{vmatrix}$$

$$= (x+y+z)(xy+yz+zx-x^2-y^2-z^2)$$

If you know even more about determinants, you will realise that the determinant measures the signed volume of the parallelepiped spanned by the three position vectors $(x,y,z)$, $(y,z,x)$ and $(z,x,y)$.

We will give two solutions. Solution 1 is probably the easiest to find under exam conditions. Solution 2 puts a spring in your step.

## Solution 1

Notice that

$$1 = x^3+y^3+z^3-3xyz = (x+y+z)(x^2+y^2+x^2-xy-yz-zx) \quad (9.1)$$

and we have $x^2+y^2+z^2 \geq xy+yz+zx$ by the rearrangement inequality (page 13) or by Cauchy-Schwarz (page 12) applied to $(x,y,z)$ and $(y,z,x)$, or just because

$$(x-y)^2+(y-z)^2+(z-x)^2 \geq 0.$$

In any event it follows that $x+y+z>0$.

Let $A = x^2+y^2+z^2$ and $B = x+y+z > 0$. Clearly $B^2 - A = 2(xy+yz+zx)$. Recast equation (9.1) in terms of $A$ and $B$. We obtain that

$$B\left(A - \frac{B^2-A}{2}\right) = 1$$

so $2AB - B^3 + AB = 2$ and therefore $3AB = B^3 + 2$. It follows that

$$3A = B^2 + \frac{2}{B}.$$

The AM–GM inequality applies to $B^2$, $\frac{1}{B}$ and $\frac{1}{B}$ and so

$$3A = B^2 + \frac{2}{B} = B^2 + \frac{1}{B} + \frac{1}{B} \geq 3\sqrt[3]{1} = 3$$

and so $A \geq 1$. This minimum value for $A$ is obtained, for example, when $(x, y, z) = (1, 0, 0)$.

## Solution 2

Consider the parallelepiped mentioned in the discussion above. It has volume 1, and all three sides have the same length $\sqrt{x^2 + y^2 + z^2}$. The volume of a parallelepiped is at most the product of its three side lengths, with equality if, and only if, it is a cuboid. In fact the volume, up to a sign, is the product of the three side lengths multiplied by the cosine of one angle and the sine of another, where these angles are natural features of the parallelepiped. We then use the fact that sine and cosine take values between -1 and 1 (inclusive), and the endpoints are simultaneously achieved precisely when the parallelepiped is a cuboid. All this will be familiar if you understand *scalar triple products*.

Therefore $(\sqrt{x^2 + y^2 + z^2})^3 \geq 1$, with equality if, and only if, the sides are mutually perpendicular. The algebraic condition for this (using a dot (scalar) product is that $xy + yz + zx = 0$.

## Afterword

As often happens, a good geometric interpretation will simplify the algebra.

# Problem 2

Let triangle $ABC$ have incentre $I$ and circumcentre $O$. Suppose that $\angle AIO = 90°$ and $\angle CIO = 45°$.

Find the ratio $AB : BC : CA$.

*[The* circumcentre *of triangle $ABC$ is the centre of the circle which passes through the vertices $A$, $B$ and $C$. The* incentre *is the centre of the circle which touches the sides $AB$, $BC$ and $CA$.]*

*[Lee Zhou Zhao, Trinity College, Cambridge]*

## Discussion

It may be quite tricky to draw a plausible diagram without knowing the answer. After some experiments, you should be able to construct something like figure 9.1.

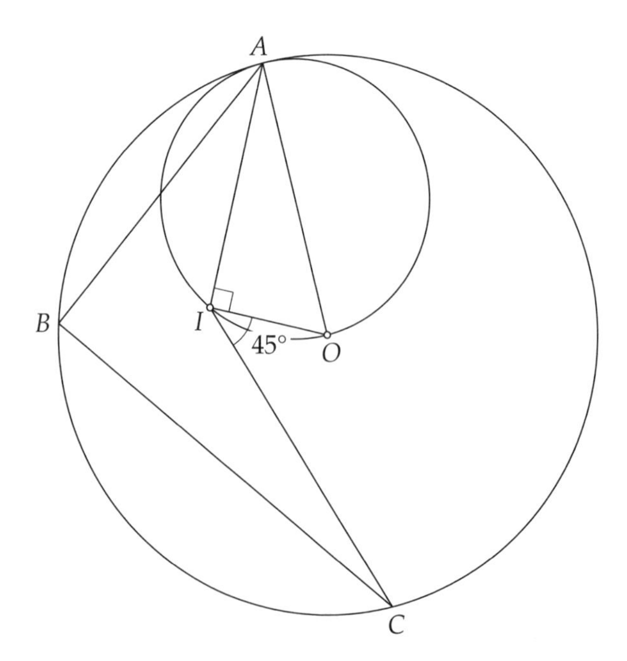


*Figure 9.1*

## Solution

See figure 9.2. In any triangle, it is routine angle chasing to establish that $\angle AIC = 90° + \frac{1}{2}B$. Angle $\angle CIO = 45°$, but no declaration about signed angle conventions has been made by the problem setters, so no careful conventions are being used. This means that $O$ is on the same side of the line $AI$ as is $C$. In a better world, the setters would have written $\angle OIC$ is equal to $45°$. We conclude that $\angle AIC = 135° = 90° + \frac{1}{2}B$ and so $B$ is a right angle. Now $AC$ is a diameter of circle $ABC$ and $O$ is its midpoint.

Produce $AI$ to meet $BC$ at $U$. Figure 9.2 is now relevant.

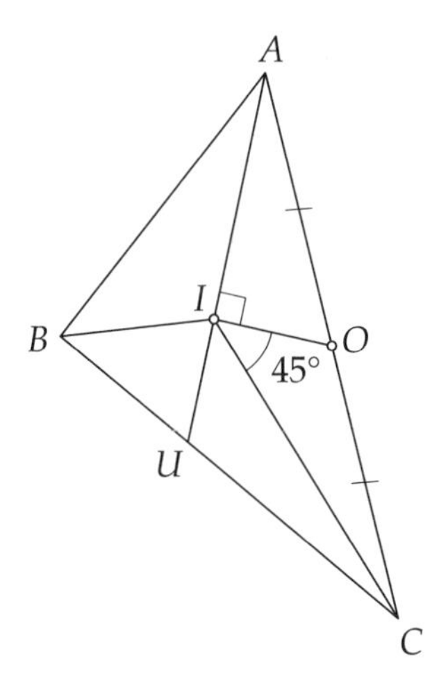


*Figure 9.2*

Now angle $\angle CIU$ is the supplement of $\angle AIC$, so $\angle CIU = 45° = \angle OIC$. Now $CI$ is the internal angle bisector at $C$, and so we have a triangle similarity $\triangle CIU \sim \triangle CIO$ by comparing angles. However, the side $CI$ is common, so this similarity is in fact an indirect congruence (*indirect* because you need to turn over the triangle).

Apply the angle bisector theorem to triangle $ABC$ using the bisector $AI$. It follows that

$$\frac{BA}{AC} = \frac{BU}{UC}.$$

However, $UC = OC = \frac{1}{2}AC$ and so $BU = \frac{1}{2}AB$.

Using the standard $a, b$ and $c$ notation for the side lengths of $ABC$, we have $2a = b + c$ and the theorem of Pythagoras tells us that $b^2 = c^2 + a^2$.

Now

$$a^2 = b^2 - c^2 = (b - c)(b + c) = 2a(b - c)$$

and so $a = 2b - 2c$. Solving this linear equation against $2a = b + c$ we discover that $5a = 4b$ and $3a = 4c$. let $a = 4\lambda$, then $b = 5\lambda$ and $c = 3\lambda$. Therefore $AB : BC : CA = 3 : 4 : 5$.

## Afterword

The famous 3, 4, 5 right-angled triangle does crop up from time to time in mathematics competitions. It is worth noting that the radius of the incircle of this triangle is 1.

The numbers 3, 4 and 5 are an example of a *Pythagorean triad*, as are the numbers 5, 12 and 13. These are the triples of positive integers which can arise as the lengths of the sides of right-angled triangles. Clearly it suffices to understand those triples which have 1 as their greatest common divisor.

It has been known since Ancient Greece that such triples are precisely those of the form $m^2 - n^2, 2mn, m^2 + n^2$ where $m > n$ are coprime positive integers of opposite parity. For example, when $m = 3$ and $n = 2$ we obtain $5, 12, 13$.

Please investigate this topic.

# Problem 3

Adrian has drawn a circle in the $xy$-plane whose radius is a positive integer at most 2008. The origin lies somewhere inside the circle.

You are allowed to ask him questions of the form "Is the point $(x, y)$ inside your circle?" After each question he will answer truthfully "yes" or "no".

Show that it is always possible to deduce the radius of the circle after at most sixty questions.

*[Any point which lies exactly on the circle may be considered to lie inside the circle.]*

*[Paul Jefferys, Trinity College, Cambridge]*

## Discussion

We have to find a strategy to get sufficient information about the circle that its integer radius is determined. Actually more is required, because the candidate needs a fairly quick proof that the strategy does indeed determine the integer radius, so the mathematics needs to be clean.

## Solution

The circle contains the origin in its interior, and so cuts the $x$ axis twice, once when $x$ is positive, and once when it is negative. Similar remarks apply to the $y$-axis. First ask about $(1024, 0)$. If that is inside the circle, ask about $(1024 + 512, 0)$; otherwise ask about $(512, 0)$. Using 12 binary chops of each half axis, so 48 questions, you can locate the crossings of the four half-axes to within intervals of length 1. By asking another 3 questions on each half axis, you can refine the uncertainty so that each cut is located in an interval of length $\frac{1}{8}$. We deem endpoints of an interval to be in that interval.

The centre of the circle is now determined to be within a square box aligned to the axes of side $\frac{1}{8}$ because, for example, the $x$-coordinate of the centre is the average of the two points where the circle crosses the $x$-axis, and these points lie within intervals of length $\frac{1}{8}$, and so their average lies within an interval of length $\frac{1}{8}$. We call this the *central box*, and we deem it to include its boundary.

Pick and fix one of the four intervals $I$ of length $\frac{1}{8}$ on a half-axis in which we have trapped a point on the circle. Consider figure 9.3.

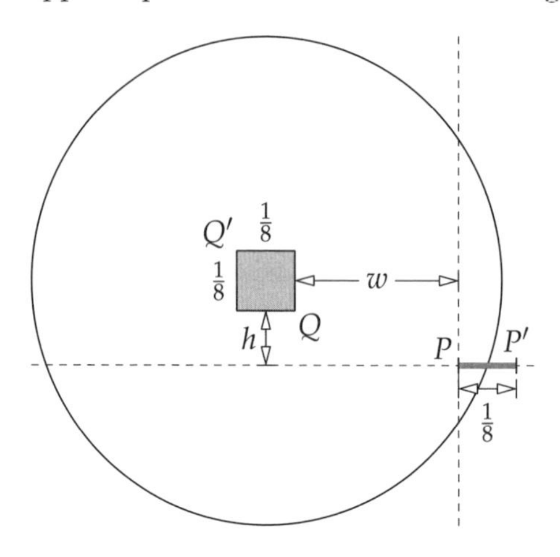


*Figure 9.3*

Choose $P$ in $I$ (possibly at an endpoint) and $Q$ in the central box to minimize the length $PQ$. Choose $w, k \geq 0$ such that the difference of the $x$-coordinates of $P$ and $Q$ is $w$, and the difference of their $y$-coordinates is $h$. Let $r_0 = |PQ|$ so $r_0^2 = w^2 + k^2$ by the theorem of Pythagoras.

Now choose $P'$ in $I$ and $Q'$ in the central box, but this time maximizing the distance $r_1 = |P'Q'|$. Now $r_1^2 \leq (w + \frac{1}{4})^2 + (h + \frac{1}{8})^2$. In order for the integral radius of the circle not to be determined by this data, there are consecutive positive integers $x - 1$ and $x$ such that $r_0^2 \leq (x-1)^2 < x^2 \leq r_1^2$. Note that $0 \leq w, h \leq x$. If the radius is not determined, then $x^2 - (x-1)^2 \leq r_1^2 - r_0^2$ so

$$2x - 1 \leq \frac{w}{2} + \frac{h}{4} + \frac{5}{64}. \tag{9.2}$$

However, if $x = 1$, then $w, h \leq 1$ so

$$2x - 1 = 1 > \frac{1}{4} + \frac{1}{2} + \frac{5}{64} \geq \frac{h}{4} + \frac{w}{2} + \frac{5}{64}.$$

If $x$ is increased by $k$, then the left-hand side increased by $2k$ and the right-hand side by at most $\frac{3}{4}k$, so inequality 9.2 never holds, irrespective of the integer radius $x$ of the circle. Therefore it is always possible to determine the integer radius of the circle by using the 60 questions.

## Afterword

Here is a method which does not work. Consider three rays (half-lines) which start at the origin, and are 120° to each other. The circle cuts each ray exactly once, and these places can be trapped in tiny intervals by using 20 binary chops on each ray.

The points where the circle cuts the ray are determined within intervals of length $\frac{4016}{2^{20}}$, and this is less than $\frac{1}{256}$. Given that the radius of the circumcircle is an integer, one might think that such an accurate determination of three points on the circle would be enough to find the radius.

However, this is incorrect, because it could be that two of the located intervals are adjacent to the origin, but the third is a long way out. There might be two points near the origin where the circle cuts rays. Indeed, one cutting point might be arbitrarily close to the origin, and the other can be as much as $\frac{1}{256}$ away on its ray (or vice versa). There is ample wriggle room to create a continuous family of circles of very different radii, by moving the two points near the origin in a continuous way, and some of these circles will have different integral radii. That is not quite a formal proof, but this is an informal discussion.

# Problem 4

Prove that there are infinitely many pairs of distinct positive integers $x$, $y$ such that $x^2 + y^3$ is divisible by $x^3 + y^2$.

*[David Monk, ex-University of Edinburgh]*

## Discussion

The form of the divisibility condition ensures that there is no hope of finding infinitely many solutions when $y$ is constant. Therefore looking for solutions where $y$ depends on $x$ seems a sensible plan. If you try the simplest possible way that $y$ might depend on $x$, then you will be rewarded.

## Solution

Let $y = kx$ for rational $k$. Then

$$\frac{x^2 + y^3}{x^3 + y^2} = \frac{k^3 x + 1}{x + k^2}.$$

We would like to find integral $x$ and $y$ so that this ratio is an integer.

Now

$$\frac{k^3 x + 1}{x + k^2} = \frac{k^3 x + 1 + k^5 - k^5}{x + k^2} = k^3 - \frac{k^5 - 1}{x + k^2}.$$

We get the required solutions by choosing $k$ to be an integer and $x$ to be a positive integer such that $x + k^2$ divides $k^5 - 1$. A simple way to do this is to let $x = k^5 - k^2 - 1$ and $y = kx$ where $k \geq 2$ is a positive integer. Note that this ensures that both $x$ and $y$ are positive integers, and that they are different.

## Afterword

I do not know of any solution which does not use the $y = kx$ trick. It does not seem unreasonable to ask people to think of this, because it is the obvious way to simplify the fractional expression in the problem.

# 2009 solutions

## Problem 1

Find all solutions in non-negative integers $a$, $b$ to $\sqrt{a}+\sqrt{b}=\sqrt{2009}$.

*[Paul Jefferys, UBS]*

### Discussion

If the integer $z$ is the square of a rational number $q$, then $q$ is an integer. An explanation is available in section 2.6.

### Solution

Suppose that $\sqrt{a}+\sqrt{b}=\sqrt{2009}=7\sqrt{41}$. Therefore $\sqrt{a}=7\sqrt{41}-\sqrt{b}$ and squaring we find that $a=2009+b-14\sqrt{41b}$. Therefore (see section 2.6 on page 29) $41b$ is the square of an integer, so $b=41t^2$ for some non-negative integer $t$. By similar reasoning, $a=41s^2$ for some non-negative integer $s$. Now

$$\sqrt{a}+\sqrt{b}=(s+t)\sqrt{41}=7\sqrt{41}$$

holds if, and only if, $s+t=7$ where $s$ and $t$ are non-negative integers. The complete list of solutions is $(a,b)=\left(41i^2,41(7-i)^2\right)$ for $i=0,1,\ldots,7$. If you want to list the solutions explicitly, they are $(0,2009)$, $(41,1476)$, $(164,1025)$, $(369,656)$, $(656,369)$, $(1025,164)$, $(1456,41)$ and $(2009,0)$.

## Afterword

We mentioned in the discussion that if the integer $z$ is the square of a rational number $q$, then $q$ is an integer. This generalizes the famous fact that $\sqrt{2}$ is not the ratio of two positive integers. Similarly it follows that if $m$ is a positive integer, then $\sqrt{m}$ is a rational number if, and only if, $m$ is a (perfect) square.

# Problem 2

Let $ABC$ be an acute-angled triangle with $\angle B = \angle C$. Let the circumcentre be $O$ and the orthocentre be $H$.

Prove that the centre of the circle $BOH$ lies on the line $AB$.

*[The* circumcentre *of triangle $ABC$ is the centre of the circle which passes through the vertices $A$, $B$ and $C$. The* orthocentre *is the point of intersection of the perpendiculars from each vertex to the opposite side.]*

*[Christopher Bradley, ex-Clifton College]*

## Discussion

It is traditional not to draw pictures when posing a geometry problem in a mathematical olympiad. Drawing a correct diagram is the responsibility of the candidate. This leaves open the possibility that more than one diagram is possible. In this problem, that is exactly the situation, and there are essentially two different possible diagrams. However, at the point of transition between the configurations, when $ABC$ is equilateral, the result is false. Unfortunately (and scandalously!) this glitch was not picked up by either the candidates or the markers of BMO2 at the time. The most common cause of multiple diagrams is that it matters whether or not a triangle has an obtuse angle.

When there are multiple diagrams, it is possible that slightly different proofs are needed to deal with the two situations. You might find yourself citing the fact that opposite angles of a cyclic quadrilateral sum to 180° in one case, and using angles in the same segment in the other.

Two questions arise.

(i) What does this mean for marking?

(ii) How can this problem be addressed or avoided?

The situation regarding (i) is unpredictable. In the UK, we do not worry very much about multiple diagrams in BMO1, but it is sometimes an issue in BMO2. Other competitions have their own policies. At the IMO, you cannot tell if the coordinators (the marking police) will regard what they call *diagram dependency* as a significant issue. Sometimes there is a small fine of 1 or 2 marks for missing a possible diagram, but often the fine is 0 marks.

As for (ii), it depends who is doing the addressing and avoiding. If it is the setters, then they can avoid multiple diagrams by being very specific in describing the configuration. When you see a problem which begins something like "The triangle $ABC$ is acute angled and $AB > AC \dots$", then you can tell that the setters are trying to avoid multiple diagrams.

From the point of view of the candidates, algebraic solutions (including trigonometric solutions) which make sense without a diagram can avoid the problem. If the diagram is irrelevant, how can marks possibly be deducted for missing a configuration? However, if the candidate is going to use classical synthetic Euclidean methods, in other words, stare at a diagram and throw theorems and similar triangles at the problem, then care is necessary. By using directed lengths and angles with ruthless consistency, it is possible to construct arguments for which the diagram is irrelevant. This requires considerable self-discipline, but it can be learned. Unsurprisingly "angles in the same segment are equal" and "opposite angles of a cyclic quadrilateral are supplementary" become fused into a single theorem in this new world.

Do not spend large amounts of time worrying about diagram dependency. If you collect a fine for lack of care, then it will usually be a small one. Only worry about this issue if you have spare time towards the end of the exam. It is better to put a 6/7 or 9/10 in the bank, and only later grub around for an extra mark when you have nothing better to do.

## Solution

See figure 10.1.

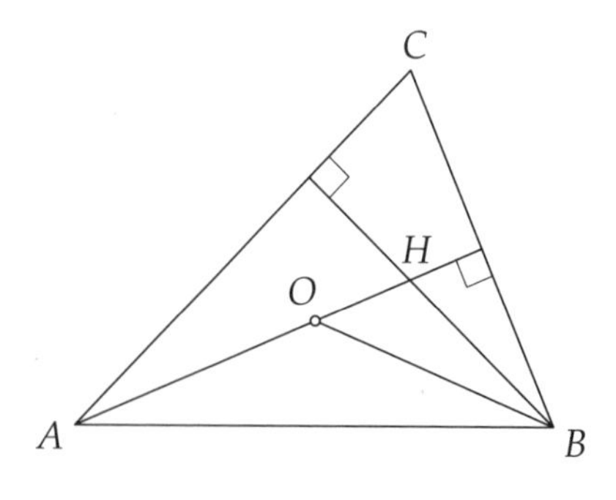


*Figure 10.1*

Note that $\angle ABO = \angle HBC$ because they are both $90° - B$. This follows by a short angle-chase which you should write out in your solution.

Choose $X$ on $AB$ so that $XO$ is perpendicular to $BO$ and let $AO$ meet $BC$ at $Y$. There are two diagrams, depending on whether $A$ is at least or less than $60°$. See figures 10.2 and 10.3. The essential change between the diagrams concerns which of $O$ or $H$ is closer to the apex $A$ of the isosceles triangle $ABC$.

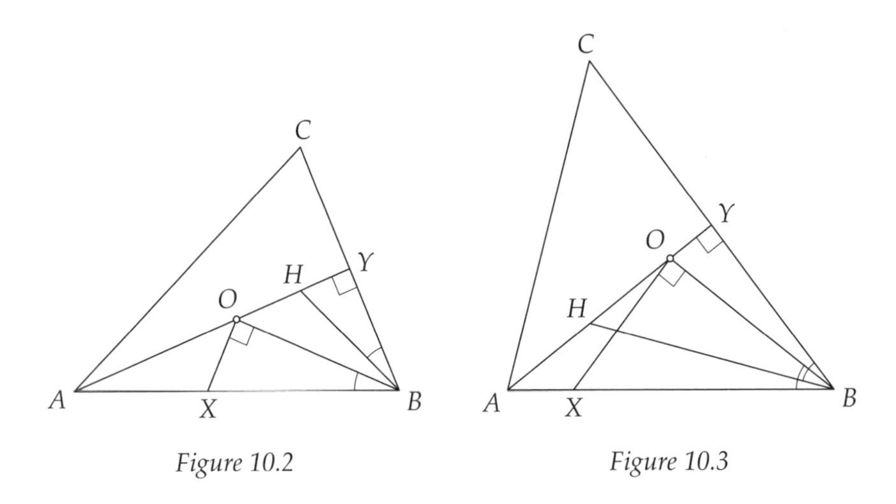


*Figure 10.2* *Figure 10.3*

First we assume that $A$ is less than $60°$. See figure 10.2.

Taking complements of equal angles $\angle ABO$ and $\angle HBC$ in the right-angled triangles $XBO$ and $HBY$ we find that $\angle YHB = \angle OXB$. Now $HOXB$ is a cyclic quadrilateral by converse of exterior angle equals interior opposite. The associated circle has $XB$ as a diameter because of the right angles it subtends at $H$ and $O$, and centre of this circle lies on $AB$.

If $\angle A$ is at least $60°$, the justification for $OHXB$ being cyclic becomes the converse of angles in the same segment, but otherwise the argument is unchanged. See figure 10.3.

When $A = 60°$, the triangle is equilateral and the result is false because $O = H$, and there are infinitely many circles passing through $B, O$ and $H$, only one of which has its centre on the line $AB$. If you regard the equilateral triangle as a limit of nearly isosceles triangles, the corresponding limit circle will have a double point of contact with the line $AO$, and this has its centre on $AB$ as required.

## Afterword

It is moot whether the markers would insist on analysing all configurations to give full marks. In fact they did not, but you can never be sure. You always have to worry that there are marks at stake.

This key property of $O$ and $H$ being used in this problem is that they are *isogonal conjugates*. See section 2.4 on page 21.

There is another very interesting way to look at this problem, via the notion of *spiral similarity*. Suppose that $LM$ and $ST$ are intervals lying in the plane. They are similar, in two ways. Let us consider the similarity which carries $L$ to $S$ and $M$ to $T$. This similarity defines a transformation of the whole plane as follows. Suppose that $Z$ is any point in the plane, then there will be a unique point $Z'$ in the plane such that the (possibly degenerate) triangle $ZLM$ is directly similar to triangle $Z'ST$. This transformation might be an enlargement (a homothety) or a translation, but if $LM$ and $ST$ are not parallel, then something more complicated is going on. In fact there will be a unique point $W$ fixed by this transformation, and the similarity can be thought of as an enlargement from $W$ followed by a rotation about $W$ (or vice versa). This result is called the *spiral similarity* theorem, and $W$ is the centre of spiral similarity for the transformation.

Usually we do not pay very much attention to similarities of intervals, but direct similarities of triangles are another matter; we get interested in them all the time, but every such similarity comes from a similarity of intervals.

You may find yourself asking, why is this true, and how do you find the centre of spiral similarity $W$? Once you know the recipe for finding $W$, it is not hard to fill in all the details and so I leave that to the reader. See figure 10.4.

You find $W$ like this: regard $LM$ and $ST$ as non-parallel lines which cross at $W'$. The circles $LW'S$ and $MW'T$ cross at $W'$ and $W$.

In the problem under consideration, we quickly find similar right-angled triangles $BYH$ and $BOX$, and the similarity transformation which sends one to the other is rotation about $B$ followed by an enlargement from $B$. Pick a pair of corresponding sides, say $YH$ and $OX$. The associated lines lines meet at $O$, so the centre of spiral similarity is at the other point of intersection of circles $YOO$ and $HOX$. The centre of spiral similarity is at $B$, so $B$ lies on $HOX$ and we can finish as before.

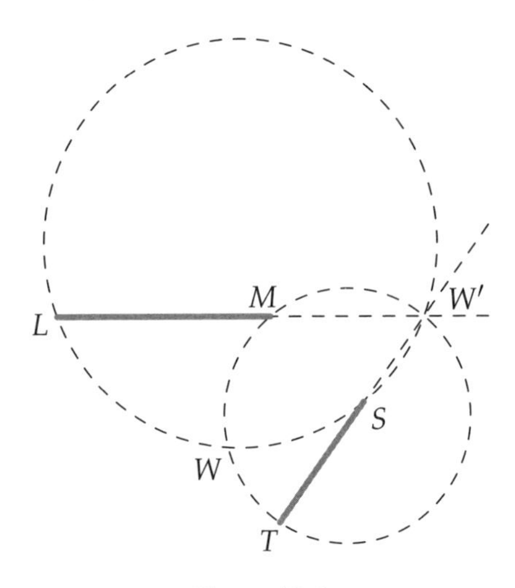


*Figure 10.4*

Now, the astute reader will have noticed something strange going on here. The point $W'$ is $O$ and the circle $YOO$ is not well defined since we have only specified two different points which lie on it. There is a double point issue here. Perturb the intervals $YH$ and $OX$ slightly without changing the lines that they define; just nudge their endpoints slightly. The point $W'$ is unchanged, the point $O$ is displaced on the line $OX$ and the point $Y$ is displaced on the line of $W'H$. As we let the perturbation shrink to zero, we see that the circle we inadequately described as $YOO$ has to pass through $Y$ and $O$, and at $O$ it is tangent to the line $OX$.

# Problem 3

Find all functions $f$ from the real numbers to the real numbers which satisfy

$$f(x^3) + f(y^3) = (x + y)(f(x^2) + f(y^2) - f(xy))$$

for all real numbers $x$ and $y$.

*[Tom Lovering, Trinity College, Cambridge]*

## Discussion

All you can do is to play, and see where it leads you.

## Solution

Put $y = -x$ and then, $f(x^3) + f(-x^3) = 0$. Every real number has a unique cube root, and so $f(-z) = -f(z)$ for all real numbers $z$. We say that $f$ is an *odd* function, and it follows that $f(0) = 0$.

Put $x = 0$ into the defining functional equation to discover that

$$f(y^3) = yf(y^2)$$

for all real numbers $y$.

For all real numbers $x$ and $y$ we have

$$xf(x^2) + yf(y^2) = f(x^3) + f(y^3) = (x + y)(f(x^2) - f(xy) + f(y^2))$$

and (replacing $y$ by $-y$)

$$xf(x^2) - yf(y^2) = f(x^3) - f(y^3) = (x - y)(f(x^2) + f(xy) + f(y^2)).$$

Adding, we obtain

$$2xf(x^2) = 2xf(x^2) - 2yf(xy) + 2x(y^2)$$

and so $yf(xy) = xf(y^2)$ for all $x$ and $y$. Put $y = 1$ and let $k = f(1)$ so $f(x) = kx$ for all real numbers $k$.

The logic has it that if $f$ is a function which satisfies our functional equation, then there is a constant $k$ such that $f(x) = kx$ for all real numbers

$x$. We have not finished the problem. It remains possible that one of the following is the case.

(i) There are no functions at all which satisfy the functional equation, and so far we have eliminated all possibilities except the functions of the form $f(x) = kx$ for a constant $k$. Perhaps if we do more work, we can eliminate those possibilities as well.

(ii) Perhaps some, but not all, of the functions of the form $f(x) = kx$ for all real numbers $x$, and we have to do more work to discover which constants $k$ give genuine solutions to the functional equation.

In fact, for any chosen value of a constant $k$, we can substitute our candidate solution into the functional equation

$$f(x^3) + f(y^3) = k(x^3 + y^3)$$

and functions are of the form

$$\begin{aligned}(x+y)\big(f(x^2) + f(y^2) - f(xy)\big) &= (x+y)\big(kx^2 + ky^2 - kxy\big)\\ &= k(x+y)\big(x^2 - xy + y^2\big)\\ &= k\big(x^3 + y^3\big).\end{aligned}$$

## Afterword

The final part, where we tested candidate solutions to see if they worked, was vital. There is always a fine (in marks) for failing to address this matter. Sometimes you can get away with "I checked that these functions worked and they do", but it is safer to actually write out the verification, in case there are markers who do not have a trusting nature. That happens a lot, and is the reason that they have been asked to be markers.

# Problem 4

Given a positive integer $n$, let $b(n)$ denote the number of positive integers whose binary representations occur as blocks of consecutive integers in the binary expansion of $n$. For example, $b(13) = 6$ because $13 = 1101_2$, which contains as consecutive blocks the binary representations of $13 = 1101_2$, $6 = 110_2$, $5 = 101_2$, $3 = 11_2$, $2 = 10_2$ and $1 = 1_2$.

Show that if $n \leq 2500$, then $b(n) \leq 39$; determine the values of $n$ for which equality holds.

*[Adrian Sanders, ex-Trinity College, Cambridge]*

## Discussion

Why 2500? Why 39? It is a safe bet that these integers have been tuned to produce a suitable answer. If you do the calculation, and get a numerical answer of no apparent significance, then you should check your arithmetic carefully, for that would be very surprising indeed.

## Solution

Let $l(n)$ denote the number of digits of the positive integer $n$ when it is written in binary, and call this number the *length* of $n$. We divide the task into studying numbers of particular length.

Note that $l(2500) = 12$ because $2048 < 2500 \leq 4096$. Suppose that $n \leq 2500$ and $l(n) = 12$. Now $2048 + 512 > 2500$ so the first three binary digits of $n$ are 100. We refer to a sequence of consecutive digits which is the binary representation of a positive integer as a substring. Substrings necessarily begin with a 1. Therefore our binary string has unique substrings of length 10, 11 and 12.

### Case (a)

Suppose that $l(n) = 12$. There are up to two substrings of length 9 (one beginning with the first digit, and possibly another beginning with the fourth digit, if that is a 1). Proceeding in this way, we find that the number of different binary substrings is at most

$$1 + 1 + 1 + 2 + 3 + 4 + 5 + 6 + 7 + 4 + 2 + 1 = 37 < 39.$$

The numbers start to fall at the end of this sum because there are only $2^{k-1}$ positive integers of length $k$, since the initial digit is 1, and subsequent digits can be 0 or 1. We are not interested in duplicated substrings, and count them only once.

**Case (b)**

Suppose that $l(n) \leq 10$; then the analysis is very similar to case (a).

$$l(n) \leq 1+2+3+4+5+6+7+8+4+2+1 = 35 \leq 39.$$

**Case (c)**

Finally we deal with the delicate case when $l(n) = 11$. Using the same arguments as before, we obtain

$$l(n) \leq 1+2+3+4+5+6+7+8+4+2+1 = 43$$

and that is not good enough, since we wish to achieve an upper bound of 39. We need to argue more carefully.

If we have a 0 $d$-digits from the right (where $4 \leq d$), that reduces the number of substrings of length $e$ by 1 for all $e$ in the range $4 \leq e \leq d$. Thus any 0 in the leftmost four digits reduces the maximum number of substrings by at least 5, so $b(n) \leq 43 - 5 = 38$. Moreover, any two zeros in the leftmost seven digits causes a reduction of 5, so again $b(n) \leq 38$. If there are three zeros in the leftmost 8 digits, they cause a reduction of 6, so $b(n) \leq 37$.

If $b(n) \geq 39$, then $n$ in binary is $111a_1a_2a_3b_1b_2b_3b_4$ where at most one $a_i$ is zero. If the string begins 1111111 then there are four occurrences of 1111, and three occurrences of 11111, which is impossible because $b(n) \geq 39$.

If the string begins 1111110, the fact that $a_3 = 0$ reduces the bound by 2, and the initial string of six 1s causes two duplicates of 1111 and one duplicate of 11111, so this cannot happen.

If the string begins 1111101, the fact that $a_2 = 0$ reduces the bound by 3, and $a_1$ causes a duplicate of 1111, so $b(n) \leq 39$.

If the string begins 1111011, the fact that $a_1 = 0$ reduces the bound by 4, so $b(n) \leq 39$.

We have now established that $b(n) \leq 39$. We now investigate to see if this bound is achieved, and if so, for which values of $n$. For the bound to be achieved we need $b_1 = 1$, else the bound would drop by 1. Therefore the candidates for $b(n) = 39$ are of the form $1111a_1a_211b_2b_3b_4$.a If $a_1 = 0$ and $a_2 = 1$, we either have a duplicate of 1111 or 1110. Therefore the candidates for achieving $b(n) = 39$ are of the form $11111011b_2b_3b_4$. If $b_2 = 1$, we will get a duplicate of 1111 or 1110. We cannot have $b_3 = 1$ else we get a duplicate of 1101. Therefore the candidates are of the form $111110110b_3b_4$. If $b_3 = 1$, then 1101 is duplicated. The remaining possibilities are 11111011000 and 11111011001.

It is a routine matter to verify that these two binary numbers do indeed have 39 (different) substrings. The values of $n$ for which $b(n) = 39$ are 2008 and 2009.

## Afterword

Perhaps this was predictable. After all, why choose the numbers in the question in that way rather than in some other way? This turns out to have been a very suitable problem to be set in the British Mathematical Olympiad which happened during the 2008-2009 academic year.

# 2010 solutions

## Problem 1

There are $2010^{2010}$ children at a mathematics camp. Each has at most three friends at the camp, and if $A$ is friends with $B$, then $B$ is friends with $A$.

The camp leader would like to line the children up so that there are at most 2010 children between any pair of friends. Is it always possible to do this?

*[Paul Jefferys, UBS]*

### Discussion

The number of atoms in the observable universe is estimated to be about $10^{80}$, so this is clearly a problem of pure mathematics. It concerns growth. It turns out to be convenient to select one child (Eve) arbitrarily, and view the social network from the point of view of that child. This simplifies the mathematics considerably, and places this problem in the category of mathematical olympiad problems where the difficulty is to realise that it is easier than it looks.

Consider the function $f$ which counts how many children are $n$ friendships away from Eve. Given that it is possible to nominate which children are friends, we can set up a social network in which it is possible to give neat formulas for $f(1), f(2), f(3)$ and so on, with these numbers growing extremely quickly. The conditions of the problem are such that the camp leader is trying to put children who are friends of friends of friends of ... of friends of Eve fairly close together, but the sequence $f(i)$ is growing so quickly that this soon becomes difficult.

## Solution

In fact this is not always possible. We are at liberty to arrange the friendships to preclude the specified arrangement of children. Select a child at the camp, and call her *Eve*.

The important idea is that the friends of Eve are close to her, and their friends are close to them, and so on. Thus if there is a chain of friendships linking two children, then this controls how far apart they can be. We arrange matters so that Eve has so many short chains of friendships that the children involved in these chains are too numerous to fit into the line as described in the question.

We define the notion of an $i$-friend. First, say that Eve is a 0-friend of herself, and that Eve has three friends which we describe as 1-friends. Then for $k \geq 1$, after the $k$-friends have been chosen, each of them is assigned two friends from among the children who are not yet $j$-friends for any $j$ provided that there are enough spare children remaining to do this. These pairs of children are all $(k+1)$-friends of Eve. When the supply of unassigned children is exhausted, the process stops. Therefore Eve need not have a full set of $m$-friends where $m$ is the label of the final collection of children being assigned friendships. See figure 11.1.

Notice that if $1 \leq n < m$, then Eve has $3 \times 2^{n-1} > 2^n$ $n$-friends. Now imagine the children as being on adjacent points of the number line, and (for contradiction) positioned so that there are at most 2010 children between any pair of friends.

The distance between Eve and each $n$-friend is at most $2011n$. They can be on each side of Eve, so there is room for $2 \times 2011n$ of them but

$$2 \times 2011n < 2 \times 2048n = 2^{12}n.$$

However if $n = 16$, there are more than $2^{16}$ $n$-friends but less than $2^{16}$ places for them to stand on the line. We need to check that there are enough children to assign two 16-friends to every 15-friend but this calculation is straightforward because

$$1 + 3 + 3 \times 2 + 3 \times 2^2 + \cdots + 3 \times 2^{15} < 2^{17}.$$

Notice that $2^{17} < 2010^{2010}$ because $2 < 2010$ and $17 < 2010$. It is possible for Eve to have a full set of 16-friends, so we have a contradiction.

This is absurd, so we have established that it is not necessarily possible to place the children in accordance with the conditions specified in the problem.

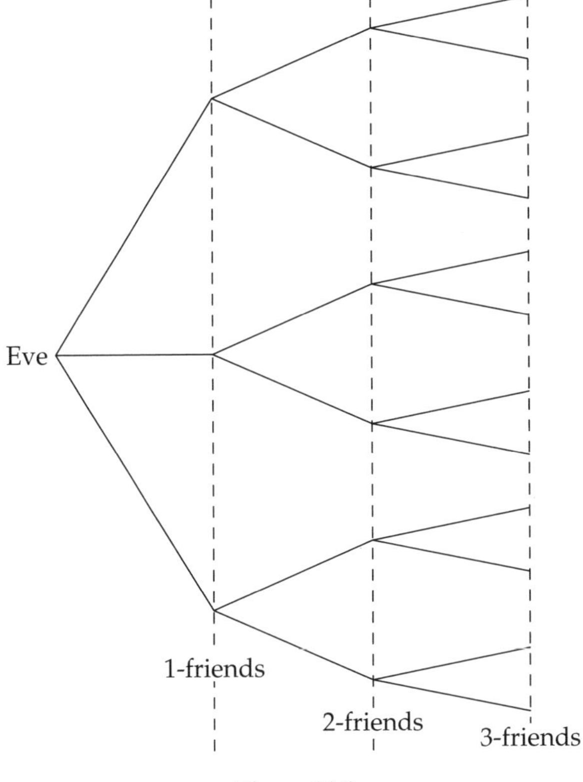


*Figure 11.1*

## Afterword

The number of $n$-friends is growing as an exponential function of $n$, but the number of places in the line to stash them is only growing as a linear function of $n$, so it is not surprising that we quickly run out of places to put the children.

Note that there are configurations of friendships which do allow the children to be arranged in a line so that there are at most 2010 children between any pair of friends. There is, for example, the sad situation that every child is friendless. A happier example can be made by lining the children up arbitrarily, and then deeming friendships to exist between neighbours, but not between other pairs of children.

# Problem 2

In triangle $ABC$ the centroid is $G$ and $D$ is the midpoint of $CA$. The line through $G$ parallel to $BC$ meets $AB$ at $E$.

Prove that $\angle AEC = \angle DGC$ if, and only if, $\angle ACB = 90°$.

*[The* centroid *of a triangle is the point of intersection of the three medians. A* median *joins a vertex to the midpoint of the opposite side.]*

*[David Monk, ex-University of Edinburgh]*

## Discussion

There is a transatlantic controversy concerning the meanings of the word trapezium and trapezoid, and a quadrilateral with a pair of parallel sides appears in the configuration. We give a solution which avoids mention of either t-word, but a student might easily wish to mention this figure in the course of a solution. We address the matter in depth in the Afterword.

This problem can be solved by straight-forward chasing of angles provided that a natural line is added to the diagram.

## Solution

Produce $CG$ to meet $AB$ at $M$. See figure 11.2.

This is a natural thing to do because everything will hang on whether $M$, the midpoint of $AB$, is the circumcentre of triangle $ABC$.

Suppose that $\angle AEC = \angle DGC$. The supplements of these angles are equal so $\angle CEB = \angle CEG$ and therefore $CGEB$ is cyclic by the converse of angles in the same segment. Now $\angle AEG = \angle BCG$ because $AEG$ is an exterior angle of the cyclic quadrilateral. However, $EG$ and $BC$ are given to be parallel, so $\angle AEG = \angle ABC$ because they are corresponding angles.

Now $\angle MBC = \angle BCM$ so triangle $MBC$ is isosceles with apex $M$. Therefore $MB = MC$, and we know that $M$ is the midpoint of $AC$ so $M$ is the circumcentre of triangle $ABC$ and $AB$ is a diameter. The theorem of angle in a semicircle (Thales) gives $\angle BCA = 90°$.

The argument is reversible, and so the problem is solved.

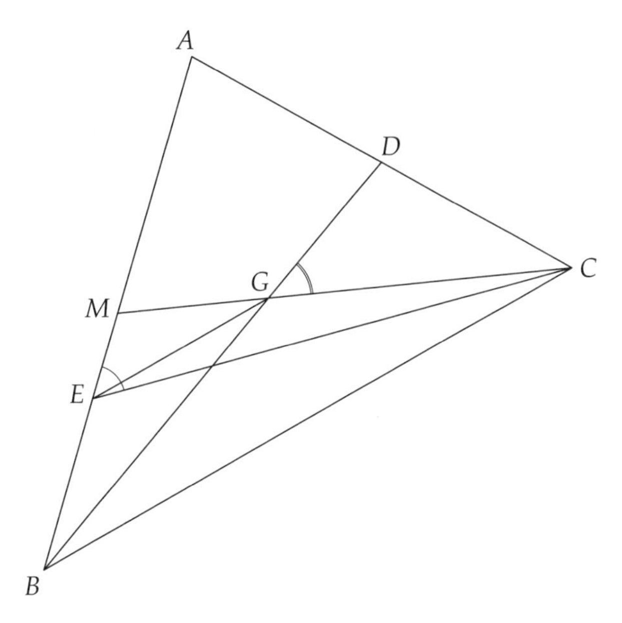


Figure 11.2

## Afterword

The quadrilateral $CGEB$ with a pair of parallel sides plays a role in this configuration. A British trapezium is a North American trapezoid. It would be a very minor matter if the Americans and Brits simply used a different word for the same thing. However, it is worse than that. The standard British usage follows the taxonomy of quadrilaterals put forward by Proclus: trapezium means exactly two parallel sides, and trapezoid means no parallel sides. Unfortunately, the two terms were accidentally transposed in Charles Hutton's *Mathematical and Philosophical Dictionary* of 1795. The error did not prosper in Britain, but it took firm hold in the USA, and it is now standard usage there.

I propose a compromise, that the words trapezium and trapezoid should henceforth be synonyms, and describe quadrilaterals which have at least one pair of parallel sides. It would then follow that a parallelogram is both a trapezium and a trapezoid, even though it does not have exactly one pair of parallel sides. Moreover, there would be no word to describe a quadrilateral which had no pair of parallel sides. This would be a triumph for Nicolas Bourbaki over Proclus.

# Problem 3

The integer $x$ is at least 3 and $n = x^6 - 1$. Let $p$ be a prime and $k$ be a positive integer such that $p^k$ is a factor of $n$.
Show that $p^{3k} < 8n$.

*[Paul Jefferys, UBS]*

## Discussion

The problem concerns the factorization of $x^6 - 1$. Notice that

$$x^6 - 1 = (x^3 - 1)(x^3 + 1)$$

and these two cubics can each be further factorized. This is a nice technical problem, and a systematic approach will bring rewards.

## Solution

Note that

$$\begin{aligned} x^6 - 1 &= (x^3 - 1)(x^3 + 1) \\ &= (x - 1)(x + 1)(x^2 + x + 1)(x^2 - x + 1). \end{aligned}$$

Therefore $n$ is the product of three quadratic factors

$$n = (x^2 - 1)(x^2 + x + 1)(x^2 - x + 1).$$

Now, loosely speaking, for large $x$ these three factors are about $\sqrt[3]{n}$. If they were pairwise coprime, then if $p^k$ divided $n$, then it would have to divide one of the quadratic factors, so $p^{3k}$ could not be much more than $n$. The balance of the argument will be to tighten this up, and to allow for the fact that these quadratic factors are not necessarily pairwise coprime, and that $x$ might not be large.

First we address pairwise coprimality or its failure:

$$\begin{aligned} \gcd(x^2 + x + 1, x^2 - x + 1) &= \gcd(2x, x^2 - x + 1) \\ &= \gcd(2, x^2 - x + 1) \\ &= 1. \end{aligned}$$

The final equality is because $x^2 - x + 1$ is odd. Next we see that

$$\begin{aligned}\gcd(x^2 + x + 1, x^2 - 1) &= \gcd(x + 2, (x - 1)(x + 1)) \\ &= \gcd(x + 2, x - 1) \\ &= \gcd(3, x - 1),\end{aligned}$$

and this is 3 or 1. Now look at the final pair:

$$\begin{aligned}\gcd(x^2 - x + 1, x^2 - 1) &= \gcd(x - 2, (x - 1)(x + 1)) \\ &= \gcd(x - 2, x + 1) \\ &= \gcd(3, x + 1)\end{aligned}$$

and this is 3 or 1.

First we deal with the simplest case, when $p$ divides at most one of the three quadratic factors. Notice that

$$x^2 - x + 1 < x^2 - 1 < x^2 + x + 1$$

since $x \geq 3$. For the same reason,

$$x + 1 < (x - 1)(x + 1) = x^2 - 1$$

and so

$$p^k < 2x^2 - 1$$

and so

$$p^k \leq 2x^2 - 2.$$

Now $p^{3k} \leq 8(x^2 - 1)^3 < 8(x^6 - 1) = 8n$.

Finally suppose that $p$ divides more than one quadratic factor, so $p = 3$ and there are two cases: either (a) 3 divides $x^2 - 1$ and $x^2 + x + 1$; or (b) 3 divides both $x^2 - 1$ and $x^2 - x + 1$.

**Case (a)**

In this case 3 divides $x - 1$ so 9 divides $(x - 1)(x + 2) = x^2 + x - 2$ and so $x^2 + x + 1 \equiv 3 \pmod 9$. Therefore $3^2$ does not divide $x^2 + x + 1$ and so $3^{k-1}$ divides $x - 1$. Now

$$3^k \leq (x + 1)(x - 1) = x^2 - 1 < 2(x^2 - 1),$$

and just as before,

$$3^{3k} = p^{3k} < 8(x^2 - 1)^3 < 8(x^6 - 1) = 8n.$$

**Case (b)**

In this case 3 divides $x+1$ so 9 divides $(x+1)(x-2) = x^2 - x - 2$ and so $x^2 - x + 1 \equiv 3 \pmod 9$. Therefore $3^2$ does not divide $x^2 - x + 1$ and so $3^{k-1}$ divides $x+1$ so

$$3^k \leq 3(x+1) \leq x(x+1) = x^2 + x < x^2 + x^2 - 2 = 2(x^2 - 1).$$

The final inequality holds because $x \geq 3$. Just as before, it follows that $p^{3k} < 8n$.

## Afterword

This is a clear example of a solution which has been polished several times. It would be a remarkable script which disposed of possibilities in such an organized fashion. You can imagine the sort of thing which happens in real marking or coordination, when a student has overlooked a detail or three, and the issue is to establish the significance of the omissions, and the level of fine which is appropriate.

# Problem 4

Prove that, for all positive real numbers $x$, $y$ and $z$,

$$4(x+y+z)^3 > 27(x^2y+y^2z+z^2x).$$

*[Adrian Sanders, ex-Trinity College, Cambridge]*

## Discussion

First we acknowledge that an almost identical question was used in the Canadian Mathematical Olympiad in 1999. This was, of course, an accident, because BMO2 questions are original compositions.

It is tempting to investigate the polynomial

$$f(x,y,z) = x^2y+y^2z+z^2x$$

which is unchanged under cyclic change of variables. We cannot immediately say "assume that $x \geq y \geq z$ because we are not allowed to permute the variables arbitrarily". However, you can do something if you observe that

$$f(x,y,z) - f(z,y,x) = (y-z)(x-y)(x-z).$$

Use cyclic change of letters to arrange that either $x \geq y \geq z$ or $z \geq y \geq x$. If the latter occurs, then $f(x,y,z) = f(z,y,x) + (y-z)(x-y)(x-z)$ and $(y-z)(x-y)(x-z) \leq 0$ so $f(x,y,z) \leq f(z,y,x)$. If you are trying to prove that $f(x,y,z)$ is bounded above by some quantity (and we are), it suffices to assume that $x \geq y \geq z$. We will not invoke this assumption in the arguments below, but there are solutions that require this manoeuvre.

## Solution 1

The only student to solve this problem in the exam, Jack Smith, used this method. Subtract the right-hand side from the left, rearrange, and you obtain

$$x(2x-4y-z)^2 + y(2y-4z-x)^2 + z(2z-4x-y)^2 \geq 0.$$

That looks like magic, but it is not. The cyclic symmetry should encourage a candidate to try to find $a, b$ and $c$ such that

$$4(x+y+z)^3 - 27(x^2y+y^2z+z^2x) = x(ax+by+cz)^2 + y(ay+bz+cx)^2 + z(az+bx+cy)^2$$

by equating coefficients. It cannot be that each of the three squares is 0, since summing it would follow that $x + y + z = 0$ which is not the case. Therefore the inequality is strict.

## Solution 2

This exquisite argument was supplied by the candidate Joshua Lam (but after the exam). Rename $x, y$ and $z$ as $A, B$ and $C$ (but not necessarily in that order) so that $A \leq B \leq C$. Now $0 < A \leq B \leq C$ so $AB \leq AC \leq BC$ and we may apply the rearrangement inequality mentioned in section 2.1. We do not know the relative sizes of $x, y$ and $z$, but

$$\begin{aligned} x^2y + y^2z + z^2x &\leq A(AB) + B(AC) + C(BC) \\ &= B(A^2 + AC + C^2) \\ &< B(A + C)^2. \end{aligned}$$

Now $B(A+C)^2 = 4B\left(\dfrac{A+C}{2}\right)^2$ and we may apply the AM–GM inequality to the three quantities $B$, $\frac{1}{2}(A+C)$ and $\frac{1}{2}(A+C)$ to discover that

$$B(A+C)^2 = 4B\left(\frac{A+C}{2}\right)^2 \leq 4\left(\frac{A+B+C}{3}\right)^3 = \frac{4}{27}(x+y+z)^3.$$

Therefore

$$4(x+y+z)^3 \geq 27B(A+C)^2 > 27(x^2y + y^2z + z^2x)$$

as required.

## Afterword

I have seen the trick used in solution 2 deployed with success elsewhere, so it is worth making sure that you understand and remember this technique.

# 2011 solutions

## Problem 1

Let $ABC$ be a triangle and $X$ be a point inside the triangle. The lines $AX$, $BX$ and $CX$ meet the circle $ABC$ again at $P$, $Q$ and $R$ respectively.

Choose a point $U$ on $XP$ which is between $X$ and $P$. Suppose that the lines through $U$ which are parallel to $AB$ and $CA$ meet $XQ$ and $XR$ at points $V$ and $W$ respectively.

Prove that the points $R$, $W$, $V$ and $Q$ lie on a circle.

*[Christopher Bradley, ex-Clifton College]*

### Discussion

It seems that every good geometry problem admits a vast multiplicity of solutions, and experience shows that mathematical olympiad candidates are blessed with such inventiveness that they discover the most extraordinary routes to solve such problems. The celebrated Hungarian mathematician Paul Erdős used to talk of *The Book* in which the Almighty kept records of optimal proofs. I suspect that the proof that follows is from The Book.

### Solution

See figure 12.1 on the next page.

Thanks to alternate angles between parallel lines (sometimes called Z-angles in the language of the street), $\angle CWU = \angle WCA$. However $\angle RPA = \angle RCA = \angle WCA$ since these angles are subtended on the circumcircle by the same arc $AR$. Now $\angle CWU = \angle RPU$ and so the quadrilateral $RPUW$

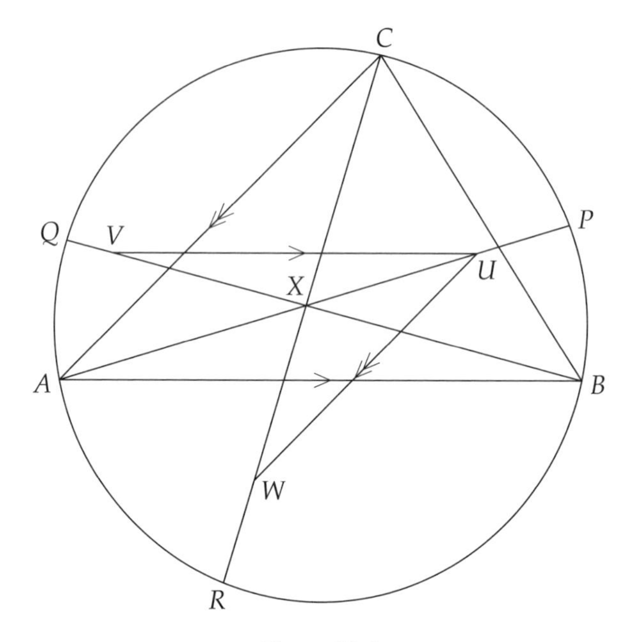


*Figure 12.1*

is cyclic. Similarly, quadrilateral $PQVU$ is cyclic. The circumcircles of these quadrilaterals have $AP$ as their radical axis. Now $X$ is on $AP$ so the power of $X$ with respect to each of the two circles is the same. See section 2.2 on page 16. In particular, $XV \times XQ = XW \times XR$, and so by the converse of the power of a point theorem (see section 2.2 on page 16) $RWVQ$ is a cyclic quadrilateral.

## Afterword

Make sure that you have a good understanding of the ideas surrounding power of a point, the tangent–secant theorem, the intersecting chords theorem, the radical axis of a pair of circles and the radical centre of three circles. A remarkable proportion of recent geometry problems at the International Mathematical Olympiad involve these ideas, and similar remarks apply to other mathematical olympiads.

# Problem 2

Find all positive integers $x$ and $y$ such that $x+y+1$ divides $2xy$ and $x+y-1$ divides $x^2+y^2-1$.

*[Paul Jefferys, UBS]*

## Discussion

This is a gem. It reworks an old idea, that integers which are close together have a small greatest common divisor.

## Solution

Suppose that $x$ and $y$ are integers which satisfy the conditions given in the problem. We have a "difference of two squares" factorization, and

$$(x+y+1)(x+y-1) = x^2+y^2-1+2xy$$

valid for all integers $x$ and $y$. The problem states that $x+y-1$ divides $x^2+y^2-1$, and so it also divides $2xy$. However, it is given that $x+y+1$ divides $2xy$ as well. These two factors of $2xy$ differ by 2, and so their greatest common divisor is at most 2. They are, informally, almost coprime. Therefore $(x+y+1)(x+y-1) \leq 4xy$ and this inequality rearranges to give $(x-y)^2 - 1 \leq 0$. Thus $x$ and $y$ are either equal or consecutive positive integers.

In fact $x = y = m$ is impossible for then $2m+1$ divides $2m^2$ and hence divides $m(2m+1) - 2m^2 = m$. However $2m+1 > 1$, so $m$ is positive and so is not divisible by $2m+1$.

On the other hand, if $x$ and $y$ are consecutive integers $m$ and $m+1$, then the divisibility conditions are indeed satisfied.

## Afterword

If $u$ and $v$ are positive integers with greatest common divisor $d$, then their lowest common multiple is $\frac{uv}{d}$. Once again we can draw powerful conclusions if $d$ is small.

# Problem 3

The function $f$ is defined on the positive integers as follows:

$$f(1) = 1;$$
$$f(2n) = \begin{cases} f(n) & \text{if } n \text{ is even;} \\ 2f(n) & \text{if } n \text{ is odd;} \end{cases}$$
$$f(2n+1) = \begin{cases} 2f(n)+1 & \text{if } n \text{ is even;} \\ f(n) & \text{if } n \text{ is odd.} \end{cases}$$

Find the number of positive integers $n$ which are less than 2011 and have the property that $f(n) = f(2011)$.

*[David Monk, ex-University of Edinburgh]*

## Discussion

For many years, David Monk would turn up at the UK IMO selection camp at Trinity College in Cambridge equipped with yet another collection of his ingenious "background problems". The students worked on these in small groups, and presented their solutions as the final act of the camp. There were often problems concerning strange functions, and this one is firmly in that excellent tradition.

## Solution

The function $f$ can be neatly described as follows. For each positive integer $n$, write $n$ in binary. Take each adjacent string of 0s or 1s, and replace it by the respective digit. Thus 1110010 becomes 1010. Finally, $f(n)$ is the value of this binary string when regarded as a binary number. Thus

$$f(1729) = f(11011000001_2) = 10101_2 = 21$$

and

$$f(42) = f(101010_2) = 101010_2 = 42.$$

We can prove that $f$ behaves as we have suggested by regarding each natural number as being written in binary. Observe that $f(1) = f(1_2) = 1_2 = 1$. If $n > 1$ then the binary representation of $n$ has at least two digits, and the final two digits are 00, 01, 10 or 11. Assume that the recipe for evaluating $f$ is correct for all positive integers which have shorter binary representations. Now the first of the five options for evaluating $f$ is the base case, and then the four subsequent options tell us that $f$ does exactly the right thing depending on the final two binary digits of $n$.

Now we address the combinatorial problem posed in the question.

$$f(2011) = f(11111011011_2) = 10101_2 = 21.$$

Regarding a binary number as beginning with an infinite string of 0s (as padding), it follows that $f(n) = 10101_2$ if, and only if, the binary representation of $n$ (including the initial padding with 0s) involves 5 changes of digit. The number of positive integers less than 2048 (that is, with at most 11 binary digits in unpadded form) which have 5 changes of digit is $\binom{11}{5} = 462$ since you can choose the places where the digits change arbitrarily. By inspecting the integers bigger than 2010 and less than 2048, we find that exactly 7 of them have 5 changes of digit: $11111011011_2$, $11111011101_2$, $11111100101_2$, $11111101001_2$, $11111101011_2$, $11111101101_2$ and $11111110101_2$. Therefore the number of positive integers $n$ such that $f(n) = f(2011)$ is $462 - 7 = 455$.

## Afterword

The important feature of 2011 is that is close to a power of 2, so that the final slightly grubby inspection is not too onerous.

# Problem 4

Let $G$ be the set of points $(x, y)$ in the plane such that $x$ and $y$ are integers in the range $1 \leq x, y \leq 2011$. A subset $S$ of $G$ is said to be *parallelogram-free* if there is no proper parallelogram with all its vertices in $S$.

Determine the largest possible size of a parallelogram-free subset of $G$.

*[A* proper parallelogram *is one where its vertices do not all lie on the same line.]*

*[Paul Jefferys, UBS]*

## Discussion

At first sight, this problem looks to be very hard. Viewing the problem using an $x, y$ coordinate plane, you can think of $G$ as a square pattern of dots. There are various ways to capture the condition that four points are the vertices of a non-degenerate parallelogram, and perhaps the most elegant is the statement that you have four non-collinear points which have the property that the midpoint of two of them is the same as the midpoint of the other two. However, even given this clean description of a non-degenerate parallelogram, it is not clear how to address the problem.

This problem falls into the *much easier than it looks* category. It is sufficient to consider parallelograms of a certain type.

## Solution

The subset $S$ of $G$ consisting of points where at least one of their coordinates is 1 has size $4021 = 2 \times 2010 + 1$. Suppose, for contradiction, that $S$ contains four points forming the vertices of a non-degenerate parallelogram. Now all points of $S$ lie on one of two mutually perpendicular lines, and since $S$ is not flat, two vertices are on the first of these lines but not the second, and the remaining two vertices are on the second line but not the first. This forces two opposite edges of the parallelogram to be perpendicular. This is an unusual but very clear absurd conclusion, and the contradiction is established.

Next we show that any subset $T$ of $G$ containing at least 4022 points contains the vertices of a parallelogram. Suppose that $T$ is such a set, and that it has $n_k$ points in row $k$. By counting horizontal gaps between the first point of $T$ in row $k$ and the other points of $T$ in the same row, we find at least $n_k - 1$ different horizontal gaps between points in row $k$. Now hang on, for I can sense the reader's furious protest that $T$ may have no points in row $k$. In that event $n_k - 1 = -1$ and we are asserting that that there are at least $-1$ different gaps in row $k$. Since $0 \geq -1$, this is correct. There is no need to fret about what happens when $n_k = 1$, because the reasoning is also sound in that case.

Now the gaps we have noted in the various rows cannot all be different, because if they were, then the total number of different gaps arising would be at least 2011 because

$$\sum_{k=1}^{2011} (n_k - 1) = \left( \sum_{k=1}^{2011} n_k \right) - 2011 = |T| - 2011 \geq 2011.$$

However,the $x$-coordinates are all between 1 and 2011, so there are at most 2010 different gaps.

Therefore at least one gap arises twice. We were careful only to count the gaps in a particular row which have a given left endpoint. Therefore these two gaps of the same length are in different rows. The set $T$ is therefore not parallelogram-free.

## Afterword

The subtle feature of this problem, and the reason that superficially it looks very hard, is that understanding parallelograms arranged at arbitrary angles seems to be a very difficult problem. The reason that the problem is accessible is that we do not need to do that. There is a configuration of 4021 points which involves no parallelogram, but any collection of 4022 points involves a parallelogram with a pair of sides parallel to the $x$-axis. This is not what one might expect. After all, there are many more parallelograms with sides not parallel to the $x$-axis than parallelograms with sides which are parallel to the $x$-axis, so you would expect parallelograms inevitably to arise after some threshold number of points, and parallelograms with sides parallel to the $x$-axis to be forced to arise at a higher threshold. The remarkable thing is that the two thresholds are the same, so that you never need to do any reasoning about parallelograms in general position. The hard aspect of this problem is realising that this extraordinary situation pertains, so that you can exploit it.

However, once you realise that working with parallelograms in general position is a hopeless enterprise, then the mathematical olympiad clue kicks in. The problem is known to be solvable in sensible time, so the parallelograms at peculiar angles are irrelevant. When doing real research mathematics, this clue is sometimes unavailable. Some problems really are hard. However, it is interesting that natural questions often have natural answers.

# 2012 solutions

## Problem 1

The diagonals $AC$ and $BD$ of a cyclic quadrilateral meet at $E$. The midpoints of the sides $AB$, $BC$, $CD$ and $DA$ are $P$, $Q$, $R$ and $S$ respectively. Prove that the circles $EPS$ and $EQR$ have the same radius.

*[David Monk, ex-University of Edinburgh]*

### Discussion

The line segment joining the midpoints of two sides of a triangle is parallel to the third side, and has half its length. This follows by a similarity argument, or with more panache, by an enlargement argument. Therefore if $ABCD$ is a quadrilateral, then the midpoints of its sides are the vertices of a parallelogram, sometimes called the Varignon parallelogram of the quadrilateral. The sides of the Varignon parallelogram are parallel to the diagonals of $ABCD$.

### Solution

As just discussed, $PS = QR$ since their lengths are both half that of $BD$. By the sine rule applied to triangles $PES$ and $REQ$, it suffices to show that the angles $\angle REQ$ and $\angle PES$ are equal or supplementary (so that their sines are equal). In fact they are supplementary. See figure 13.1 on the following page.

We have indirectly similar triangles $AED \sim BEC$ by angle considerations (using same segment twice, and vertically opposite too if you wish to use both belt and braces). The points $Q$ and $S$ are matched up

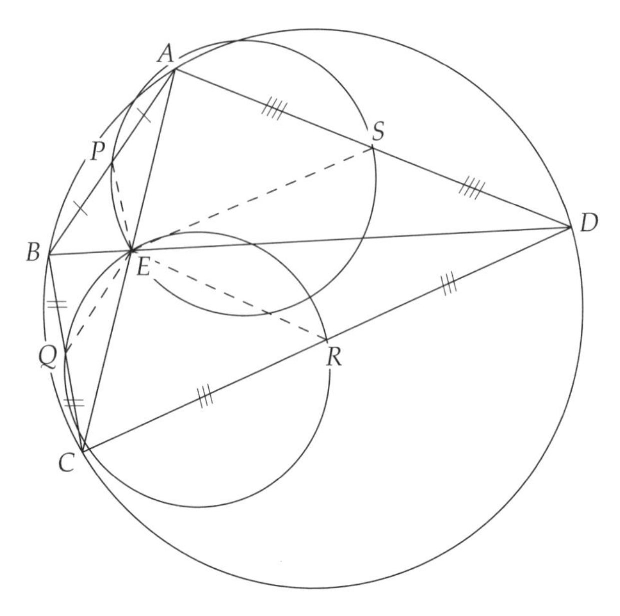


*Figure 13.1*

by the similarity, since they are the midpoints of corresponding sides. Therefore $\angle AES = \angle QEB$ and $\angle SED = \angle CEQ$. By analogous arguments $\angle PEA = \angle DER$ and $\angle BEP = \angle REC$. It follows that

$$\begin{aligned}\angle REQ + \angle PES &= \angle REC + \angle CEQ + \angle PEA + \angle AES \\ &= \angle DER + \angle REC + \angle CEQ + \angle QEB \\ &= \angle DEB \\ &= 180^\circ.\end{aligned}$$

Thus $\angle REQ$ and $\angle PES$ are supplementary and the two circles mentioned in the problem have the same radius by the sine rule.

## Afterword

By symmetry it follows that the circumcircles of triangles $SER$ and $QEP$ have the same radius. There are now three radii in play, including that of the circle $ABCD$. Perhaps there is an interesting relationship between these radii?

Start afresh. Consider a fixed parallelogram $PQRS$. What is the locus of points $E$ such that $\angle PES$ and $\angle REQ$ are supplementary? Suppose that $E$ is such a point. Are there concyclic points $A$, $B$, $C$ and $D$ giving rise to $P$, $Q$, $R$, $S$ and $E$ as in this problem?

# Problem 2

A function $f$ is defined on the positive integers by $f(1) = 1$ and, for $n > 1$,

$$f(n) = f\left(\left\lfloor \frac{2n-1}{3} \right\rfloor\right) + f\left(\left\lfloor \frac{2n}{3} \right\rfloor\right)$$

where $\lfloor x \rfloor$ denotes the greatest integer less than or equal to $x$.

Is it true that $f(n) - f(n-1) \leq n$ for all $n > 1$?

*[Here are some examples of the use of $\lfloor x \rfloor$: $\lfloor \pi \rfloor = 3$; $\lfloor 1729 \rfloor = 1729$; $\left\lfloor \frac{2012}{1000} \right\rfloor = 2$.]*

*[David Monk, ex-University of Edinburgh]*

## Discussion

The candidate who is systematic and organized will be rewarded. Getting a firm grip on $f(n) - f(n-1)$ is clearly the way to proceed. The function which assigns the value $\lfloor x \rfloor$ to the real number $x$ is usually called the *floor function*, though once it was often called the *integer part function*. The graph of this function looks like a staircase with the verticals missing. There is an associated function which assigns to each real number $x$ the smallest integer which is not less than $x$. This is called the *ceiling function*, and the value of the ceiling function applied to the real number $x$ is written $\lceil x \rceil$. The graphs of the floor and ceiling functions are very similar, but are not exactly the same of course. Note that $\lfloor x \rfloor = \lceil x \rceil$ if, and only if, $x$ is an integer.

## Solution

We are given that $f(1) = 1$, and use the recurrence $f(2) = f(1) + f(1) = 2$. Now for $n > 2$ we have $n = 3k$, $3k + 1$ or $3k + 2$ for a suitable positive integer $k$.

If $n = 3k$, then

$$f(3k) = f\left(\left\lfloor \frac{6k-1}{3} \right\rfloor\right) + f\left(\left\lfloor \frac{6k}{3} \right\rfloor\right) = f(2k-1) + f(2k)$$

If $n = 3k + 1$, then

$$f(3k+1) = f(2k) + f(2k) = 2f(2k).$$

If $n = 3k + 2$, then

$$f(3k+2) = f(2k+1) + f(2k+1) = 2f(2k+1).$$

Now we can describe the differences:

$$\begin{aligned} f(3k+2) - f(3k+1) &= 2(f(2k+1) - f(2k)) \qquad (13.1) \\ f(3k+1) - f(3k) &= f(2k) - f(2k-1); \\ f(3k) - f(3k-1) &= f(2k) - f(2k-1). \end{aligned}$$

Equation (13.1) looks likely to be helpful in showing that $f(n) - f(n-1)$ can be bigger than $n$, because $3k+2$ and $3k+1$ are about $\frac{3}{2}$ times as large as $2k$ and $2k-1$, but the difference between the values of $f$ at consecutive arguments is increasing by a factor of 2. Ideally, you would have a long chain of applications of equation (13.1) when calculating $f(n) - f(n-1)$.

For example $f(8) - f(7) = 2(f(5) - f(4)) = 4(f(3) - f(2))$ and $f(3) - f(2) = f(2) - f(1) = 1$. Therefore $f(8) - f(7) = 4 < 8$, and we have not found an $n$ for which $f(n) - f(n-1) \geq n$. A longer chain of applications of equation (13.1) would be helpful, but this one cannot be extended because 7 is odd.

Suppose that $x$ is a positive integer, then to allow equation (13.1) to be deployed using $x$ as $2k$, it is necessary and sufficient that $x$ be even. For it to to be deployed twice it is necessary and sufficient that $\frac{3}{2}x + 1$ be even, or rather that $3x + 2$ be a multiple of 4, or equivalently $x \equiv 2 \pmod 4$. We have done the base case of a inductive proof that equation (13.1) can be deployed $n$ times in succession on $x$ if, and only if, $x \equiv -2 \pmod{2^n}$.

For the inductive step, it is necessary and sufficient that $\frac{3}{2}x + 1$ satisfy the condition that $n - 1$ applications of equation (13.1) can be made, so

$$\tfrac{3}{2}x + 1 \equiv -2 \pmod{2^{n-1}},$$

or equivalently

$$3x \equiv -6 \pmod{2^n},$$

or rather

$$x \equiv -2 \pmod{2^n}.$$

The inductive proof is complete. It seems that 2, 6, 14, 30 and 62 are promising places to look.

$f(31) - f(30) = 8$ by a direct calculation using our equations, but then off we go:

$$\begin{aligned} f(47) - f(46) &= 16 \text{ by equation (13.1);} \\ f(71) - f(70) &= 32 \text{ by equation (13.1);} \\ f(107) - f(106) &= 64 \text{ by equation (13.1);} \\ f(161) - f(160) &= 128 \text{ by equation (13.1);} \\ f(242) - f(241) &= 256 \text{ by equation (13.1).} \end{aligned}$$

We knew that we could apply equation (13.1) five times in a row because $30 = 2^5 - 2$, and we have found that $f(242) - f(241) > 242$.

If instead we start with 14, we do not succeed because we can calculate that $f(15) - f(14) = 1$, and four applications of equation (13.1) yields $f(80) - f(79) = 2^4 = 16$. However, $16 < 80$. It was very helpful that equation (13.1) is deployed three times during the calculation of $f(31) - f(30)$, giving $f(31) - f(30) = 2^3 = 8$.

## Afterword

This problem has echoes of the *Collatz conjecture*. Suppose that $m$ is a positive integer. If $m$ is even, then halve it. If it is odd, then multiply it by 3 and add 1. The conjecture asserts that successive applications of this rule will produce 1 after a finite number of steps. For example:

$$7, 22, 11, 34, 17, 52, 26, 13, 40, 20, 10, 5, 16, 8, 4, 2, 1.$$

Such sequences are sometimes called *hailstone sequences* because of an erudite meteorological analogy with the hailstone formation process. Several people other than Lothar Collatz have posed this conjecture independently, including the major mathematical personalities Helmut Hasse, Shizuo Kakutani, Sir Bryan Thwaites and Stanislaw Ulam. By a curious coincidence, Bryan Thwaites was UK team leader at the International Mathematical Olympiad at the 12th competition, held in Hungary in 1970.

Hailstone sequences are very soothing exercises in mental arithmetic. They induce sleep far more effectively than ovine enumeration.

# Problem 3

The set of real numbers is split into two subsets which do not intersect. Prove that for each pair $(m, n)$ of positive integers, there are real numbers $x < y < z$ all in the same subset such that $m(z-y) = n(y-x)$.

*[Alan Slomson, University of Leeds]*

## Discussion

It may be helpful to think of this problem geometrically, using real numbers as labels for points on the number line. What is the role of $q = \dfrac{n}{m}$ in this context? This is a problem where it may be helpful to do a special case first, and then use that as a tool to finish the problem.

## Solution

The condition $m(z-y) = n(y-x)$ is equivalent to $z - y = q(y-x)$ where $q = \dfrac{m}{n}$. We can think of this as a relationship between intervals rather than just their lengths; the interval $[x, y]$ is enlarged from $x$ with scale factor $q$ to have the same length as $[y, z]$, and then it can be translated until the intervals coincide.

Let the two given subsets of $\mathbb{R}$ be $S$ and $T$, so $S \cup T = \mathbb{R}$ and $S \cap T = \varnothing$. It turns out to be helpful first to address the special case $q = 1$. We seek to show that either $S$ or $T$ contains an arithmetic progression $x < y < z$ of length 3, or equivalently that either $S$ or $T$ contains two different numbers and their average.

If $S$ is finite, then $T$ clearly contains such an arithmetic progression. Now suppose that $S$ is infinite, but does not contain an arithmetic progression $x < y < z$ of length 3. Choose any $a, b \in S$ with $a < b$. Let $d = b - a$, so $S$ cannot contain $a - d$, $\frac{1}{2}(a+b)$ or $b + d$ else it would contain an arithmetic progression of length 3. Therefore $a - d$, $\frac{1}{2}(a+b)$ and $b + d$ are in $T$. Now $a - d < \frac{1}{2}(a+b) < b + d$ is an arithmetic progression of length 3.

Now we move to study the general case, where $q$ is any positive rational number. In fact the rationality of $q$ is irrelevant, and it could be any positive real number. One of the two sets, say $S$, contains an arithmetic progression of length 3: $u - v < u < u + v$. Suppose that $S$ does not contain points

$x, y$ and $z$ as specified in the problem. Then $S$ cannot contain any of the following three points: $u + qv$, $u + v + qv$ and $u + v + 2qv$, so they all belong to $T$. However put $x = u + qv$, $y = u + v + qv$ and $z = u + v + 2qv$, then $x < y < z$ and $z - y = qv = q(y - x)$. Therefore $T$ contains three points $x, y, z$ as specified in the question.

## Afterword

There is a sophisticated way to solve this problem using an advanced theorem of combinatorics due to van der Waerden. It is a theorem of Ramsey theory. Here is one formulation: suppose that the positive integers are split into two subsets $U$ and $V$, so $U \cup V$ is the set of positive integers and and $U \cap V$ is the empty set. Given that $k$ is a positive integer, it follows that either $U$ or $V$ contains a $k$-term arithmetic progression with positive common difference.

Note that this result does not say that either $U$ or $V$ contains an infinite arithmetic progression, but it does follow that either $U$ or $V$ contains arithmetic progressions of arbitrary finite length.

You can solve this BMO2 problem by using van der Waerden's Theorem. We use the notation $\mathbb{N}$ for the set of positive integers (so for us, $0 \notin \mathbb{N}$, a controversial policy in parts of continental Europe). Let $U = S \cap \mathbb{N}$ and $V = T \cap \mathbb{N}$. The sets $U$ and $V$ satisfy the conditions so van der Waerden's theorem can be applied. There is an arithmetic progression of positive integers containing $m + n + 1$ terms contained in either $U$ or $V$. Let this arithmetic progression be

$$a, a + k, \ldots, a + mk, \ldots, a + (m + n)k.$$

Let $x = a$, $y = a + mk$ and $z = a + (m + n)k$. Then $m(z - y) = mnk = n(y - x)$, and either all terms of this arithmetic progression are in $S$, or they are all in $T$.

This theorem is definitely outside the unofficial and informally defined syllabus of secondary school level mathematics competitions. However, there are young mathematicians with precocious knowledge of advanced results, and people who know an advanced theorem have every right to deploy it, provided that they state it properly and check that its conditions are satisfied.

# Problem 4

Show that there is a positive integer $k$ with the following property: if $a$, $b$, $c$, $d$, $e$ and $f$ are integers and $m$ is a divisor of

$$a^n + b^n + c^n - d^n - e^n - f^n$$

for all integers $n$ in the range $1 \leq n \leq k$, then $m$ is a divisor of $a^n + b^n + c^n - d^n - e^n - f^n$ for all positive integers $n$.

*[Geoff Smith, University of Bath]*

## Discussion

It seems likely that the natural generalization holds for any even number of letters. It is relatively straightforward to handle the version with just 2 letters, and the choice of 6 letters is actually there to encourage the candidate to find a solution which will work for any even number of letters, and not depend on accidents available in small situations.

## Solution

Consider the polynomial

$$p(x) = (x-a)(x-b)(x-c)(x-d)(x-e)(x-f)$$

of degree 6. Each of $a, b, c, d, e$ and $f$ is a root of $p(x)$. When this product of six linear factors is multiplied out, we obtain

$$p(x) = x^6 + p_5x^5 + p_4x^4 + p_3x^3 + p_2x^2 + p_1x^1 + p_0.$$

Here $p_5 = -(a+b+c+d+e+f)$ and $p_0 = abcdef$, and the other coefficients take longer to describe. Now $a$ is a root of $p(x)$ so

$$p(a) = 0 = a^6 + p_5a^5 + p_4a^4 + p_3a^3 + p_2a^2 + p_1a^1 + p_0.$$

Multiplying by $a^j$ where $j$ is a non-negative integer, we see that

$$0 = a^{6+j} + p_5a^{5+j} + p_4a^{4+j} + p_3a^{3+j} + p_2a^{2+k} + p_1a^{1+j} + p_0a^j$$

for all integers $j \geq 0$.

Therefore the sequence $(a^i)$ (where $i \geq 0$) satisfies the recurrence

$$y_{n+6} = -p_5 y_{n+5} - p_4 y_{n+4} - p_3 y_{n+3} - p_2 y_{n+2} - p_1 y_{n+1} - p_0 y_n$$

for all $n \geq 0$. There is nothing special about $a$, and so the sequences consisting of the powers of $b$, $c$, $d$, $e$ and $f$ also satisfy this recurrence. However, the term-by-term sum (or difference) of sequences satisfying such a recurrence will satisfy the recurrence. This includes the sequence $(z_i)$ for $i \geq 0$ defined by $z_i = a^i + b^i + c^i - d^i - e^i - f^i$. Now, suppose that $m$ is a positive integer and that $m$ divides $z_1, z_2, z_3, z_4$ and $z_5$. Of course $m$ divides $z_0$ because $z_0 = 0$. Therefore $m$ divides the first 6 terms of $(z_i)$ $(i \geq 0)$. Now the recurrence provides an inductive proof that $m$ divides $z_i$ for all $i \geq 0$.

Therefore choosing $k$ to be 5 is sufficient to guarantee that all terms will be divisible by $m$.

## Afterword

In such problems, it is sometimes helpful to consider the recurrence while working in the integers modulo $n$ for some suitable positive integer $n$. In the above proof, we could have finished by working modulo $m$. If $p$ is a prime number, then using such sequences allows Fermat's little theorem to come into play: for all integers $a$ we have $a^p \equiv a \pmod{p}$, and if $p$ does not divide $a$, then $a^{p-1} \equiv 1 \pmod{p}$.

Note that this technique was also deployed to solve 2004/3.

The relationships between sums of powers of quantities, and the symmetric polynomials in those quantities are known as Newton's identities or the Newton-Girard formulas.

# 2013 solutions

## Problem 1

Are there infinitely many pairs of positive integers $(m, n)$ such that both $m$ divides $n^2 + 1$ and $n$ divides $m^2 + 1$?

*[Geoff Smith, University of Bath]*

### Discussion

This question was used in the feature film $X + Y$ also known as *A Beautiful Young Mind*. The leading character Nathan Ellis muses about this problem while sitting the film version of BMO2. To approach this question, you could test small pairs of positive integers to spot cases where both divisibility statements hold. Once you have done this, look to see if you can find a pattern which potentially involves infinitely many pairs of positive integers $(m, n)$ satisfying the conditions. Then set about proving that the pattern actually works.

### Solution

This problem revolves around the Fibonacci sequence $F_1, F_2, F_3, \ldots$, which is defined by $F_1 = F_2 = 1$ and

$$F_{i+2} = F_{i+1} + F_i \tag{14.1}$$

for all $i \geq 1$. The initial fragment of this sequence is

$$1, 1, 2, 3, 5, 8, 13, 21, 34, \ldots$$

so $F_1 = 1$, $F_3 = 2$, $F_5 = 5$, $F_7 = 13$ and $F_9 = 34$. One could define $F_0$, and even extend the sequence backwards using negative integers as subscripts by using the recurrence (14.1), and it then follows that $F_j + F_{-j}(-1)^i = 0$ for all integers $j$. The negative subscripts become very useful if we are considering the Fibonacci sequence when performing modular arithmetic.

The connection with our problem is that, by experiment, it seems that pairs of terms of the Fibonacci sequence with adjacent odd subscripts might always work. For example 13 divides $5^2 + 1$ and 5 divides $13^2 + 1$. Put formally, we conjecture that $F_{2u-1}, F_{2u+1}$ is always a solution. In fact this is correct. There is a well-known formula (the Cassini identity):

$$F_{v+1}F_{v-1} - F_v^2 = (-1)^v$$

for all positive integers $v$ (and let $F_0 = 0$). This can either be quoted or proved by induction on $v$. When $v = 2u$, this tells us that $F_{2u-1}F_{2u+1} = F_{2u}^2 + 1$.

Next we verify that $F_{2u-1}, F_{2u+1}$ is always a solution. Working modulo $F_{2u-1}$ we have

$$F_{2u+1}^2 + 1 \equiv (F_{2u} + F_{2u-1})^2 + 1 \equiv F_{2u}^2 + 1 \equiv F_{2u-1}F_{2u+1} \equiv 0.$$

Working modulo $F_{2u+1}$ we have

$$F_{2u-1}^2 + 1 \equiv (F_{2u+1} - F_{2u})^2 + 1 \equiv F_{2u}^2 + 1 \equiv F_{2u-1}F_{2u+1} \equiv 0.$$

## Afterword

This discussion may be skipped by people who know nothing of matrix algebra. Given $2 \times 2$ matrices

$$P = \begin{pmatrix} a & b \\ c & d \end{pmatrix} \text{ and } Q = \begin{pmatrix} w & x \\ y & z \end{pmatrix},$$

their product is defined to be

$$PQ = \begin{pmatrix} aw + by & ax + bz \\ cw + dy & cx + dz \end{pmatrix}.$$

This definition facilitates the formation of powers of such a matrix, via $P^n = PP^{n-1}$. It is helpful to define $P^0$ to be the $2 \times 2$ identity matrix, and if $P$ has an inverse matrix, it can be denoted $P^{-1}$, and this opens up the possibility of giving meaning to $P^{-n}$ where $n$ is a positive integer. This is $(P^{-1})^n$, which is the same thing as $(P^n)^{-1}$. Such matrix multiplication does not have a general commutative law $PQ = QP$, but that may happen for particular matrices $P$ and $Q$. Matrix multiplication is an associative operation, so if $P, Q$ and $R$ are $2 \times 2$ matrices, then $(PQ)R = P(QR)$, and so both can be written as $PQR$ without ambiguity. Addition of matrix is defined entry by entry, which means that

$$P + Q = \begin{pmatrix} a+w & b+x \\ c+y & d+z \end{pmatrix}.$$

Multiplication interacts with addition in familiar ways, and there are two distributive laws

$$P(Q+R) = (PQ) + (PR) \text{ and } (Q+R)P = (QP) + (RP).$$

We borrow the convention that multiplication takes priority over addition, and write the distributive laws as

$$P(Q+R) = PQ + PR \text{ and } (Q+R)P = QP + RP$$

for all $2 \times 2$ matrices $P$, $Q$ and $R$. If we work with $3 \times 3$, or $n \times n$ matrices instead, similar laws hold.

Now let us become specific and concrete. Define the Fibonacci matrix to be

$$F = \begin{pmatrix} 1 & 1 \\ 1 & 0 \end{pmatrix}.$$

It follows by induction on $i$ that

$$F^i = \begin{pmatrix} F_{i+1} & F_i \\ F_i & F_{i-1} \end{pmatrix}$$

for all positive integers $i$.

The determinant of a $2 \times 2$ matrix

$$P = \begin{pmatrix} a & b \\ c & d \end{pmatrix}$$

is $\det P = ad - bc$, and the determinant function has the wonderful property that

$$\det(AB) = \det A \det B$$

for all $2 \times 2$ matrices $A$ and $B$, and by induction, the determinant of any product of $2 \times 2$ matrices is the product of their determinants. In particular

$$\det(F^i) = (\det F)^i = (-1)^i$$

and so

$$F_{i+1}F_{i-1} - F_i^2 = \det(F^i) = (-1)^i$$

for all $i$, and we recover the Cassini identity. Other helpful identities are available. For example, if $m$ and $n$ are positive integers, then $F^{m+n} = F^m F^n$. Equate entries, and get very useful formulas.

# Problem 2

The point $P$ lies inside triangle $ABC$ so that $\angle ABP = \angle PCA$. The point $Q$ is such that $PBQC$ is a parallelogram.

Prove that $\angle QAB = \angle CAP$.

*[Andrew Jobbings, Arbelos]*

## Discussion

This is an example of a geometry problem where a good construction seems to be crucial to making progress. So think hard about what to add to the diagram to open up the scope for geometric arguments. This is quite tricky, because at first sight, there seem to be several attractive candidates for additional features.

## Solution

Note that there is only one diagram, since we are told that $P$ is inside triangle $ABC$.

Construct a point $R$ so that the quadrilateral $RPCA$ is a parallelogram. In particular, $RP$ is parallel to $AC$. See figure 14.1 on the next page.

Then, from that parallelogram we get $\angle ARP = \angle PCA$, and as we are given that $\angle PCA = \angle ABP$ we deduce that $PARB$ is a cyclic quadrilateral.

Also note that $RA$ is equal in length and parallel to $PC$, and in turn $PC$ is equal in length and parallel to $BQ$, in both cases because we are dealing with opposite edges of a parallelogram. It follows that $ARBQ$ is a parallelogram, and $RB$ is parallel to $AQ$. Therefore $\angle PAB = \angle PRB$. But $\angle PRB = \angle CAQ$, since $RP$ is parallel to $AC$ and $RB$ to $AQ$.

Now $\angle PAB = \angle CAQ$, and subtracting $\angle QAP$ from each side, we obtain $\angle QAB = \angle CAP$ as required.

## Afterword

In hindsight, adding an extra parallelogram seems very sensible. Putting a parallelogram in the figure is part of the construction, and parallelograms have all sorts of features which open up geometrical arguments. However, it is easy to be wise after the event, and finding a useful construction is a tricky business.

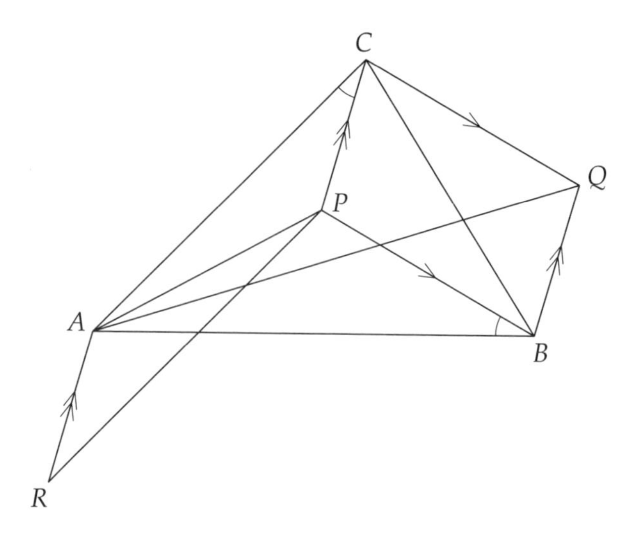


*Figure 14.1*

The isogonal conjugacy of the lines $AP$ and $AQ$ is at the heart of this problem. See section 2.4 on page 21. This diagram surfaced again as part of the configuration in Problem 2 of EGMO 2016 (the *European Girls' Mathematical Olympiad*). The EGMO jury were informed of this fact, but decided to use the question anyway.

# Problem 3

Consider the set of positive integers which, when written in binary, have exactly 2013 digits and more 0s than 1s. Let $n$ be the number of such integers and let $s$ be their sum.

Prove that, when written in binary, $n+s$ has more 0s than 1s.

*[Jeremy King, Tonbridge School]*

## Discussion

One can calculate $n$ in terms of a binomial coefficient, that is to say an entry in Pascal's triangle. On no account even think about expressing the binomial coefficient as a number written in base 10. Leave it in the form $\binom{m}{r}$ for suitable $m$ and $r$. Then find a way to relate $s$ and $n$ in such a way that, after some algebra, you can express $n+s$ in terms of a binomial coefficient and some powers of 2. Then stare hard at what you have discovered.

## Solution

Note that $2013 = 1 + 1005 + 1007$. We say that a binary strings is *good* if has length 2013, begins with a one, and involves at least 1007 zeros. Therefore each good string consists of a one followed by 2012 digits of which at most 1005 can be ones.

The total number positive integers which have binary representations of length 2013 (and begin with a one) is $2^{2012}$. To count the good strings, we exclude those involving 1007 ones and 1006 zeros, and then divide by 2. Therefore

$$n = \frac{1}{2}\left(2^{2012} - \binom{2012}{1006}\right) = 2^{2011} - \binom{2011}{1005}. \qquad (14.2)$$

Now we calculate $s$. Consider the $\binom{2012}{k}$ good strings involving exactly $k+1$ ones where $0 \le k \le 1005$. When $k=0$ there are no ones after the first position. Otherwise any given position (after the first) will contain a one in $\binom{2011}{k-1}$ cases.

Note that the binary string consisting of 2012 ones represents the integer $2^{2012} - 1$ because one followed by 2012 zeros represents $2^{2012}$.

The value of $s$ is obtained by adding the ones in our collection of good strings, each weighted by the power of 2 appropriate to its position. Imagine the good strings written under one another in a form appropriate for a huge manual addition to calculate $s$. In any column other than the first, there are

$$\sum_{k=1}^{1005} \binom{2011}{k-1}$$

ones. We will not alter the sum if we permute the positions of ones and ones in each column so that the ones appear at the top. Our calculation of $s$ then simplifies to

$$s = 2^{2012}n + (2^{2012} - 1) \sum_{k=1}^{1005} \binom{2011}{k-1}.$$

The sum indexed by $k$ is almost the first half of a row of Pascal's triangle, where the full row sums to $2^{2011}$, so

$$\sum_{k=1}^{1005} \binom{2011}{k-1} + \binom{2011}{1005} = 2^{2010}$$

so

$$\sum_{k=1}^{1005} \binom{2011}{k-1} = 2^{2010} - \binom{2011}{1005}.$$

Now

$$s = 2^{2012}n + (2^{2012} - 1)\left(2^{2010} - \binom{2011}{1005}\right).$$

Recall equation (14.2). Therefore

$$\begin{aligned} n + s &= (2^{2012} + 1)\left(2^{2011} - \binom{2011}{1005}\right) + (2^{2012} - 1)\left(2^{2010} - \binom{2011}{1005}\right) \\ &= 2^{4023} + 2^{4022} + 2^{2011} - 2^{2010} - 2^{2013}\binom{2011}{1005} \\ &= 2^{4023} + 2^{4022} - 2^{2013}\binom{2011}{1005} + 2^{2010}. \end{aligned}$$

The binary representation of this positive integer ends 001 and then 2010 zeros. This binary string has length at most 4024 and the only way it could fail to contain more zeros than ones is if it were to begin with a string of 2011 ones. However, it is less than $2^{4023} + 2^{4022} + 2^{4021}$, and so either the binary string has length less than 4024, or there is a zero in the second or third position from the left. Either way, this binary string contains more zeros than ones.

## Afterword

Performing the precise algebra necessary to get a correct answer under exam conditions would be amazing. Still, we live in a world where some people can solve *Rubik's cube* while juggling with it, so perhaps nothing is impossible.

# Problem 4

Suppose that $ABCD$ is a square and that $P$ is a point which is on the circle inscribed in the square.
Determine whether or not it is possible that $PA$, $PB$, $PC$, $PD$ and $AB$ are all integers.

*[Jeremy King, Tonbridge School]*

## Discussion

Recall the theorem of Apollonius which relates the lengths of the sides of a triangle to the length of its medians (see page 82). We temporarily forget the problem, and regard $ABC$ is a general triangle with $a$, $b$ and $c$ the lengths of its sides in the usual positions. Let the median through $A$ have length $u$ and let $v = \frac{1}{2}a$. Then

$$b^2 + c^2 = 2u^2 + 2v^2.$$

Now restore the problem to your memory.

## Solution

See figure 14.2.

Let the common centre of the square and the circle be $O$. Suppose that the radius of the circle is $r = \frac{1}{2}AB$. The point $P$ is on the circle. Apply the theorem of Apollonius to triangle $PCA$. Then $PA^2 + PC^2 = 2r^2 + 2(r\sqrt{2})^2 = 6r^2$ and so

$$2PA^2 + 2PC^2 = 3AB^2.$$

Now, suppose, for contradiction, that it is possible that $PA, PC$ and $AB$ are all integers. Among all such configurations, assume that we have one where $AB$ is as small as possible. The squares of integers are 0 or 1 modulo 3, so both $PA$ and $PC$ are multiples of 3. It follows that $AB^2$ is a multiple of 3 and therefore of 9. Divide through by 9 to see that

$$2\left(\frac{PA}{3}\right)^2 + 2\left(\frac{PC}{3}\right)^2 = 3\left(\frac{AB}{3}\right)^2.$$

Thus if we take the original square, and enlarge all lengths by a factor of $\frac{1}{3}$, then we obtain another configuration with integer distances, but

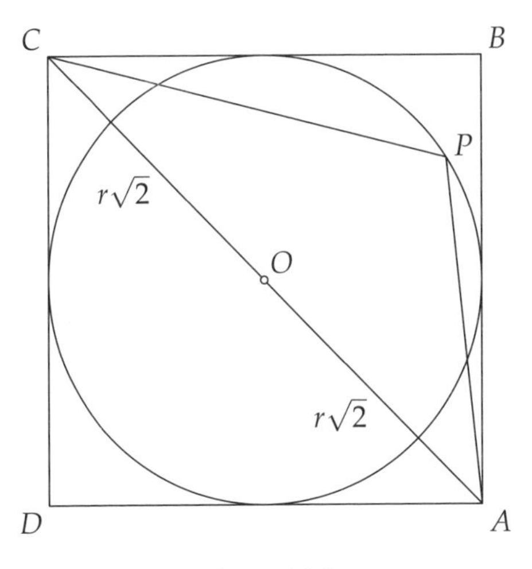


*Figure 14.2*

the side length of the square is smaller than before. This is absurd by the minimality of the integer length $AB$. Therefore it is not possible for $PA, PC$ and $AB$ all to be integers.

## Afterword

This Problem 4 was correctly placed on the paper. Our solution had two phases. First we ignored two of the corners of the square, and obtained a Diophantine equation (that is to say, we were interested in integral solutions of this equation). Then we used a contradiction argument based on a looking at a smallest counterexample. Another way to phrase this argument is to observe that any example of positive integers $x, y$ and $z$ such that $2x^2 + 2y^2 = 3z^2$ gives rise to another example but with $z$ being replaced by a smaller positive integer. Repeating this procedure indefinitely (that is, forever) yields an infinite sequence of positive integers, each term smaller that its predecessor. This is clearly impossible, and so the hypothesis that there are such positive integers $x, y$ and $z$ was wrong.

Put this way, we are using Fermat's method of infinite descent.

# 2014 solutions

## Problem 1

Every diagonal of a regular polygon with 2014 sides is coloured in one of $n$ colours. Whenever two diagonals cross in the interior, they are of different colours.

What is the minimum value of $n$ for which this is possible?

*[Richard Freeland, Trinity College, Cambridge]*

### Discussion

To be clear, the standard use of the word "diagonal" does not include the edges of the figure. Such questions, where you need to show that a minimum (or maximum) takes a certain value, are often really two problems (so just like *if, and only if* problems, you need to do both parts). In the abstract, the common way to proceed is to show that the minimum is at least $x$, and also show that the minimum is at most $x$. Then you can conclude that the minimum is $x$.

In this case a good way to start is correctly to guess the value of $x$. This should be an informed guess, so look at several examples before choosing your candidate. You need to then produce an argument that any colouring which complies with the conditions uses at least $x$ colours, and also exhibit a colouring which involves just $x$ colours. Thus there is a lack of symmetry in the style of the argument: first you get an inequality one way by a mathematical argument, and then you obtain the inequality the other way by simply exhibiting a specific colouring. This demonstration of a particular colouring is a disguised version of the reversed inequality.

## Solution

There are 1007 diagonals passing through the centre, and so they are all assigned different colours. It is possible to construct a colouring using only these 1007 colours. From each vertex, consider all diagonals which attach that vertex to another vertex on the left side of the long diagonal from that vertex, from the point of view of an observer at that vertex. Each such sinister diagonal is assigned the same colour as the long diagonal through that vertex.

It is clear that diagonals of the same colour do not meet in the interior. It is easy to "see" that each diagonal is coloured, but perhaps the easiest way to give a convincing proof is by counting. There are $\frac{1}{2}(2014 \times 2011)$ diagonals in total because there are 2011 diagonals through each vertex, and 2014 vertices, but each diagonal has two ends.

We have assigned 1007 colours to diagonals, and each colour decorates one long diagonal, and $2 \times 1005$ others. Now

$$1007(1 + 2 \times 1005) = \frac{1}{2}(2014 \times 2011)$$

so we have coloured all the diagonals. We illustrate the colouring method on a regular octagon in figure 15.1.

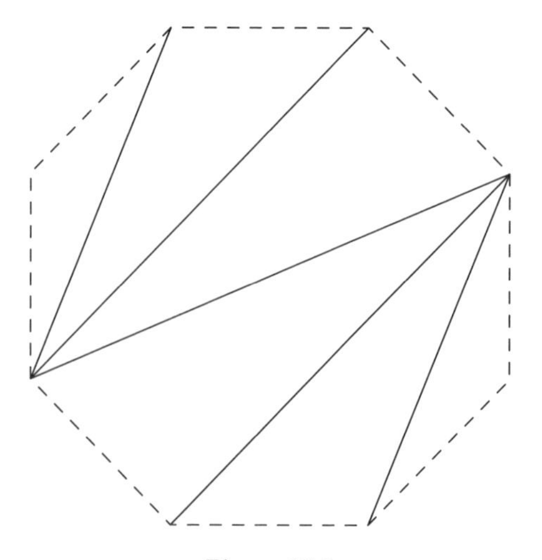

*Figure 15.1*

## Afterword

In summary: guess the lower bound, show that it is a bound, and show that you cannot do better. Except, and this does not matter, this is not the order in which we laid out the argument. We guessed a bound. We showed that you cannot do better (by considering the diagonals crossing at the centre), and finally we showed that it was achievable (by showing that a legal colouring using 1007 colours is available).

# Problem 2

Prove that it is impossible to have a cuboid for which the volume, the surface area and the perimeter are numerically equal.

*[The* perimeter of a cuboid *is the sum of the lengths of all its twelve edges.]*

*[Jeremy King, Tonbridge School]*

## Discussion

It is a general rule that students come up with a wide variety of solutions to problems involving geometry and inequalities. I suspect that this is connected with the common strategy which people use in these areas; just play around until you find something interesting, then use that to make progress. In the case of Euclidean geometry, you have the advantage of being able to draw an excellent diagram to give yourself a clue. For inequalities, you do not have such an advantage. You start by wondering if you should try to assemble some combination of the famous standard inequalities, or perhaps change the variables in an intelligent way, or perhaps you should seek a geometric interpretation from which the inequality can be deduced. It is possible that a naive sum of squares approach is all you need. It often happens that more than one of these approaches will work, but that one way leads to a short, fast solution.

## Solution

Let the three dimensions of the box be $x, y$ and $z$. Suppose, for contradiction, that

$$4(x+y+z) = 2(xy+yz+zx) = xyz.$$

Divide through by $xyz$ to obtain

$$4\left(\frac{1}{xy}+\frac{1}{yz}+\frac{1}{zx}\right) = 2\left(\frac{1}{x}+\frac{1}{y}+\frac{1}{z}\right) = 1.$$

Now

$$\begin{aligned}\tfrac{1}{4} &= \left(\frac{1}{x}+\frac{1}{y}+\frac{1}{z}\right)^2\\ &= \left(\frac{1}{x^2}+\frac{1}{y^2}+\frac{1}{z^2}\right)+2\left(\frac{1}{xy}+\frac{1}{yz}+\frac{1}{zx}\right)\\ &> 2\left(\frac{1}{xy}+\frac{1}{yz}+\frac{1}{zx}\right)\\ &= \tfrac{1}{2}.\end{aligned}$$

Therefore $\frac{1}{4} > \frac{1}{2}$ which is absurd.

## Afterword

There are very many other ways to solve this problem, and the reader is invited to discover some of them.

# Problem 3

Let $a_0 = 4$ and define a sequence of terms using the formula $a_n = a_{n-1}^2 - a_{n-1}$ for each positive integer $n$.

(a) Prove that there are infinitely many prime numbers which are factors of at least one term in the sequence;

(b) Are there infinitely many prime numbers which are factors of no term in the sequence?

*[Jeremy King, Tonbridge School]*

## Discussion

Part (a) is not too hard, and by itself would make a sensible easier problem in a less demanding competition. Part (b) requires a good idea. The standard notation for a sequence with terms $x_i$ is $(x_i)$, and it often left vague as to whether the first term is $x_0$ or $x_1$. If this is an important matter, it needs to be specified separately. This question concerns a sequence $(a_i)$ where $i \geq 0$.

## Solution

(a) We are given that $a_0 = 4 > 2$. Suppose that $a_i > 2$, then $a_{i+1} - a_i = a_i^2 - 2a_i = a_i(a_i - 2) > 2(a_i - 2) > 0$ for every $i$. Therefore $a_{i+1} > 2$, and we can employ an induction argument to prove that the sequence is strictly increasing. Also note that $a_i$ divides $a_{i+1}$ for every $i \geq 1$, so the collection of prime numbers which divides $a_i$ never gets smaller as $i$ increases. Notice that $a_i - 1 \geq 2$ and is coprime to $a_i$. Therefore $a_i - 1$ has a prime number $p$ in its factorization, and of course $p$ divides $a_{i+1}$ but not $a_i$. Therefore the number of prime divisors of terms of the sequence increases by at least 1 at every step. The set of prime numbers which divide at least one term of the sequence is therefore infinite.

(b) Let $b_i = a_i - 2$ and consider the sequence $(b_i)$. The joy of this sequence is that, by being displaced from the sequence $(a_i)$ by 2, it is impossible for an odd prime number to divide both $a_i$ and $b_i$, for it would have to divide their difference. The other attractive feature of the sequence $(b_i)$ is that it satisfies a recurrence similar to the sequence $(a_i)$, a recurrence which guarantees that that a prime divisor of $b_i$ is a prime divisor of $b_{i+1}$. That is all very well, but how on earth can you know this?

Unless you are on good terms with the magical maths fairy who will tell you to make this definition of $b_i$, you will have to do some work. Look for a definition of $b_i$ as $a_i + k$ such that $b_i$ divides $b_{i+1}$. Thus you look for integers $k$ and $c$ such that $b_{n+1} = b_n(b_n + c)$ for every $n$. In other words, you require that, for every $n$,

$$a_n^2 - a_n + k = a_n^2 - a_n + (2k + c + 1)a_n + k^2 + ck.$$

You have to unpack the algebra to see that. You choose $c$ so that $2k + c + 1 = 0$, so $c = -2k - 1$, and to make the constants balance you then need to insist that $k^2 + 2k = 0$. This gives either $k = 0, c = -1$ which of course we knew about already, or more usefully $k = -2$ and $c = 3$. We recover the definition of $b_i$ as $a_i - 2$ and then $b_{i+1} = b_i(b_i + 3)$.

Now the sequence $(a_i)$ is increasing, so $(b_i)$ is also increasing. This time one needs to be slightly more delicate when asserting that a prime divisor of $b_i + 3$ cannot be a prime divisor of $b_i$, because of the possibility that 3 might divide $b_i$. However, $b_1 = 2$, and the inductive definition of $b_i$ ensures that no $b_i$ is a multiple of 3, and so no $b_i + 3$ can be a multiple of 3 either. Thus, at each step, when you select a prime divisor of $b_i + 3$, it is definitely not 3, and so cannot be a prime divisor of $b_i$ else it would divide $b_i + 3 - b_i = 3$. Thus we produce infinitely many prime numbers, each of which divides $a_i - 2$ for sufficiently large subscripts $i$. Discarding 2 if necessary, we have infinitely odd prime numbers with this property, none of which can divide any $a_i$.

## Afterword

Perhaps there is a method to dispose of part (b) which does not involve constructing an auxiliary sequence. One can imagine a solution which runs like this: *any prime number which divides a term of the original sequence has a certain property, and there are infinitely many prime numbers which do not have that property*. Please let me know if you find such a solution.

# Problem 4

Let $ABC$ be a triangle and $P$ be a point in its interior.
Let $AP$ meet the circumcircle of $ABC$ again at $A'$. The points $B'$ and $C'$ are similarly defined.
Let $O_A$ be the circumcentre of $BCP$. The circumcentres $O_B$ and $O_C$ are similarly defined.
Let $Q_A$ be the circumcentre of $B'C'P$. The circumcentres $Q_B$ and $Q_C$ are similarly defined.
Prove that the lines $O_AQ_A, O_BQ_B$ and $O_CQ_C$ are concurrent.

*[Gerry Leversha, ex-St Paul's School]*

## Discussion

As usual, very many solutions are possible. Those who enjoy the method of inversion can deploy it with hope of success. There is also a method which draws upon the *isogonal conjugacy* of the circumcentre $O$ and orthocentre $H$ of a triangle. See section 2.4 on page 21. Figure 15.2 shows the obtuse case and figure 15.3 the acute case.

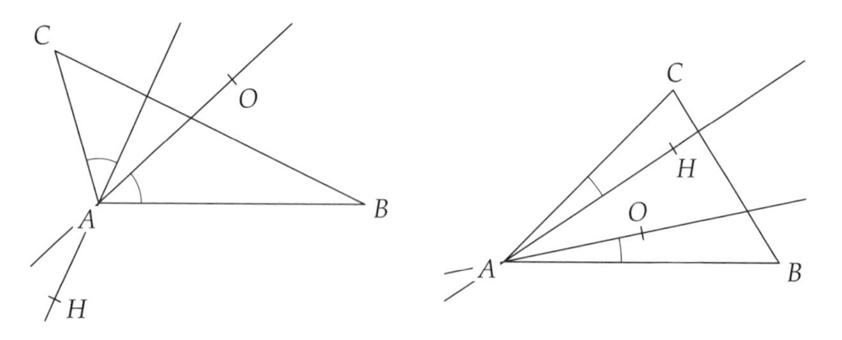


*Figure 15.2* *Figure 15.3*

The lines $AO$ and $AH$ are symmetrically placed as shown. Each one is the reflection of the other in both the internal and the external angle bisector at $A$. Moreover, $O$ and $H$ do not discriminate between vertices, so similar facts pertain at $B$ and $C$. The reader can verify all this by chasing angles.

We say that $O$ and $H$ are isogonally conjugate. The reader who has not met this terminology before is urged to investigate.

## Solution

Consider a cyclic quadrilateral $ABCD$ with circumcentre $O$. Let $P$ be the intersection of the diagonals. The respective circumcentres of triangles $DAP$ and $BCP$ are $O_1$ and $O_2$. The orthocentre of $DAP$ is $H_1$. See figure 15.4.

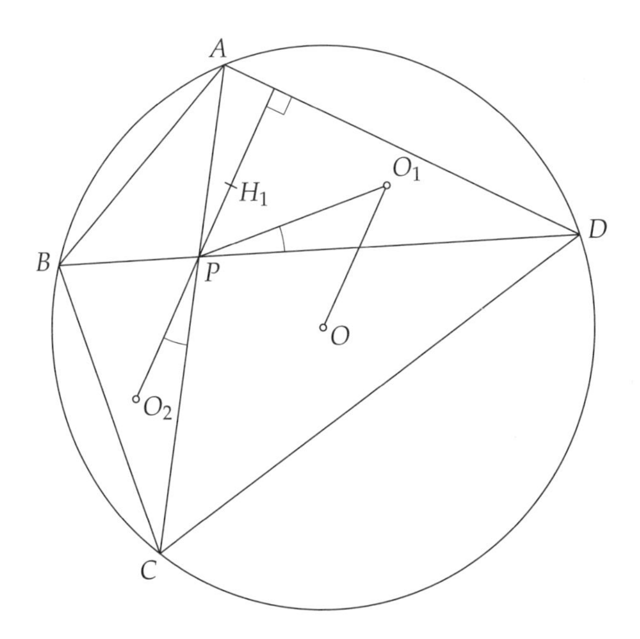


*Figure 15.4*

Triangles $APD$ and $BPC$ are indirectly similar by two applications of angle in the same segment. Therefore $\angle O_1PD = \angle CPO_2$. Also $O_1$ and $H_1$ are isogonally conjugate in triangle $APD$ so $H_1$ lies on the line $O_2P$ and so $O_2P$ is perpendicular to $AD$.

Now $O$ and $O_1$ are both on the perpendicular bisector of $AD$, so $O_2P$ is parallel to $OO_1$. By symmetry $O_1P$ is parallel to $OO_2$. Therefore $PO_2OO_1$ is a parallelogram. The diagonals of a parallelogram bisect each other, so $O_1O_2$ passes through the midpoint of $OP$.

Now we turn to the problem. Consider the cyclic quadrilateral $BCB'C'$. Then $O_1 = O_{A'}$ and $O_2 = O_A$. Therefore $O_AO_{A'}$ bisects $OP$. Similarly $O_BO_{B'}$ and $O_CO_{C'}$ both bisect $OP$ and the midpoint of $OP$ is the required point of concurrency.

## Afterword

There is a nice solution by inversion, and the interested reader is urged to invert the diagram with respect to a circle with centre $P$. The theorem of Desargues will then be useful. The theorem of Desargues belongs to projective geometry.

Here is the theory. Suppose that $A_1B_1C_1$ and $A_2B_2C_2$ are triangles in the same plane.

We say that these triangles are *in perspective from a point* $P$ if the lines $A_1A_2$, $B_1B_2$ and $C_1C_2$ concur at the point $P$. This is projective geometry, so it is allowed to have the lines $A_1A_2$, $B_1B_2$ and $C_1C_2$ parallel, and $P$ is then a point at infinity.

We say that these triangles are *in perspective from a line* $l$ if the three points where $A_1B_1$ meets $A_2B_2$, where $B_1C_1$ meets $B_2C_2$ and where $C_1A_1$ meets $C_2A_2$ all lie on $l$. Once again, it is possible that these lines are parallel and so, in the sense of projective geometry, meet at a point at infinity.

The theorem of Desargues states that $A_1B_1C_1$ and $A_2B_2C_2$ are in perspective from a point if, only if, they are in perspective from a line.

There is a direct approach to our problem (without inversion) which relies on the theorem of Desargues. It is not hard to show that $O_AO_B$ is parallel to $O_{A'}O_{B'}$ (they are both perpendicular to the line $CPC'$). Similar results apply by cyclic change of letters. Therefore (similar) triangles $O_AO_BO_C$ and $O_{A'}O_{B'}O_{C'}$ have parallel corresponding sides. In terms of projective geometry, this means that that they are in perspective from the line at infinity. It follows that they are in perspective from a point. Therefore the lines $O_AO_{A'}$, $O_BO_{B'}$ and $O_CO_{C'}$ all pass through a point $P$. We have not quite finished unfortunately, because it could be that $P$ is a point at infinity and the lines $O_AO_{A'}$, $O_BO_{B'}$ and $O_CO_{C'}$ are parallel. Further work is needed to eliminate this possibility. You can avoid the theorem of Desargues by defining $P$ to be the centre of the enlargement which yields the similarity of $O_AO_BO_C$ and $O_{A'}O_{B'}O_{C'}$. However, there is still a wrinkle because of the possibility that these triangles are congruent, so that they are related by a translation rather than an enlargement. That possibility needs to be discounted.

# 2015 solutions

## Problem 1

The first term $x_1$ of a sequence is 2014. Each subsequent term of the sequence is defined in terms of the previous term. The iterative formula is

$$x_{n+1} = \frac{(\sqrt{2}+1)x_n - 1}{(\sqrt{2}+1) + x_n}.$$

Find the 2015th term $x_{2015}$.

*[Karthik Tadinada and Dominic Rowland, St Paul's School]*

### Discussion

It is completely clear how to begin. Either you have a wonderful idea straight away, or you perform some experiments. The value of the first term is going to be important, but do not get drawn into doing nasty arithmetic. Perhaps leave it as $x_1$ for the moment, or call it $c$ if you dislike subscripts.

If you are looking for the magic bullet—the wonderful idea—then look at the shape of the formula that defines the sequence. Does it remind you of something?

### Solutions

To simplify the algebra, let $\alpha = \sqrt{2}+1$ so $\alpha^2 = 2\alpha + 1$.

We now address the concern that at some point the denominator is 0 and the procedure is illegitimate. For that to happen, we would need

$x_n = -\alpha$. It is a routine matter to work back through earlier terms of the sequence, and the reversed sequence, starting with $-\alpha$ is

$$-\alpha, -1, -\frac{1}{\alpha}, 0, \frac{1}{\alpha}, 1, \alpha$$

and there is no possible predecessor for $\alpha$. Therefore division by 0 is not an issue for us, since none of these numbers is 2014.

## Solution 1

We give a solution which relies on investigative skills rather than trigonometric insight. For $n > 1$ we have

$$x_{n+2} = \frac{\alpha x_{n+1} - 1}{\alpha + x_{n+1}} = \frac{\alpha\left(\frac{\alpha x_n - 1}{\alpha + x_n}\right) - 1}{\alpha + \alpha\left(\frac{\alpha x_n - 1}{\alpha + x_n}\right)} = \frac{(\alpha^2 - 1)x_n - 2\alpha}{\alpha^2 - 1 + 2\alpha x_n} = \frac{x_n - 1}{x_n + 1}.$$

The composition of two steps is more attractive than a single step. It would be a bad idea to look at the composition of three steps when you have the option to go straight for four steps. For $n > 1$ we have

$$\begin{aligned} x_{n+4} &= \frac{x_{n+2} - 1}{x_{n+2} + 1} \\ &= \frac{\frac{x_n - 1}{x_n + 1} - 1}{\frac{x_n - 1}{x_n + 1} + 1} \\ &= \frac{-1}{x_n} \end{aligned}$$

and so $x_{n+8} = x_n$. Therefore the sequence has period 8, so

$$x_{2015} = x_7$$

and it is routine to calculate that $x_7 = -\dfrac{2015}{2013}$.

## Solution 2

Here is an alternative proof, accessible to people with a certain trigonometric flair. Just as there are addition formulas for sine, cosine and tangent, there is one for cotangent.

$$\cot(A + B) = \frac{\cot A \cot B - 1}{\cot A + \cot B} \qquad (16.1)$$

for all $A$ and $B$ (except that you had better not divide by 0). This can be derived in a moment from the formula for $\tan(A+B)$ by taking reciprocals. Since the current reader has self-identified as having trigonometric flair, they will certainly know that $\cot\frac{\pi}{8} = \sqrt{2}+1$, and if they seek reassurance that they have remembered this correctly, assistance is at hand by putting $A = B = \frac{1}{8}\pi$ in equation (16.1). Let $\theta_n$ be the unique real number in the range $0 < \theta_n < \pi$ such that $\cot(\theta_n) = x_n$. Please remind yourself of the shape of the graph of the cotangent function, to convince yourself that there is a unique such $\theta_n$, no matter what the value of $x_n$.

Now

$$\cot(\theta_{n+1}) = \frac{\cot(\frac{\pi}{8})\cot(\theta_n) - 1}{\cot(\frac{\pi}{8}) + \cot(\theta_n)} = \cot\Big(\theta_n + \frac{\pi}{8}\Big).$$

Now cotangent is a periodic function with period $\pi$, and $2015 - 1$ is two less than a multiple of 16, so

$$x_{2015} = \cot(\theta_{2015}) = \cot\Big(\theta_1 - \frac{\pi}{4}\Big).$$

Now we use equation (16.1) and the fact that cotangent, like tangent, is an odd function. Therefore

$$x_{2015} = \frac{2014+1}{1-2014} = -\frac{2015}{2013}.$$

## Afterword

The recurrence looks unappealing at first sight, and calculating $x_2$ does not bode well. However, the determined candidate who accurately finds $x_3$ will know that she is on the right track. Also note the value of writing $\alpha = \sqrt{2}+1$; if you do not use some such trick, then there will be unpleasantness.

# Problem 2

In Oddesdon Primary School there are an odd number of classes. Each class contains an odd number of pupils. One pupil from each class will be chosen to form the school council.

Prove that the following two statements are logically equivalent.

(i) There are more ways to form a school council which includes an odd number of boys than ways to form a school council which includes an odd number of girls.

(ii) There are an odd number of classes which contain more boys than girls.

*[Jeremy King, Tonbridge School]*

## Discussion

Part of the battle is somehow to fit all this information about oddness together in your head, and the setter has deliberately made it worse by the choice of an irrelevant but distracting name for the school. Let us start by deciding to rename the school with the empty name. The style of this problem is to bamboozle the candidates, and in this context the setter has been clever enough to create lots of confusion at the outset.

## Solution

Label the classes $1, 2, \ldots$ for convenience. Let $b_i$ and $g_i$ be the numbers of boys and girls (respectively) in class $i$. Consider the polynomial $f(t)$ in $t$ defined by

$$f(t) = \prod_i (b_i + tg_i).$$

The reason to consider $f(t)$ is that the coefficient of $t^k$ is the number of ways to form a school council containing exactly $k$ girls. Here $f(t)$ is an example of a generating function, a handy gadget which captures information about a combinatorially defined sequence in a polynomial, or in other contexts, a power series.

The number of ways to form a council with an odd number of girls is the sum of the coefficients of the odd powers of $t$. There are an odd number of classes, and so an odd number of representatives on the school council. Therefore a school council contains an odd number of boys if, and only if, it contains an even number of girls. Therefore the number of ways to form a school council with an odd number of boys is the sum of the coefficients of the even powers of $t$.

First we show that condition (i) implies condition (ii). Condition (i) is equivalent to the assertion that $f(-1) > 0$, or equivalently that $\prod_i (b_i - g_i) > 0$ which implies that there are an even number of classes containing more girls than boys, which is equivalent to saying that there are an odd number of classes containing more boys than girls, so condition (ii) holds. The proof in this direction does not require the hypothesis that each class contains an odd number of pupils.

Finally assume condition (ii) holds. Since each class has odd size, it follows that $b_i - g_i \neq 0$ for every $i$. Now there are an odd number of classes, so there are an even number of classes with $b_i - g_i < 0$. Therefore $f(-1) > 0$ and so condition (i) holds.

## Afterword

It is perfectly possible to do this problem without the use of a generating function, but the use of this device does make the proof spectacularly fast and easy to follow.

# Problem 3

Two circles touch one another internally at $A$. A variable chord $PQ$ of the outer circle touches the inner circle.

Prove that the locus of the incentre of triangle $AQP$ is another circle touching the given circles at $A$.

*[The* incentre *of triangle ABC is the centre of the circle which touches the sides AB, BC and CA. A* locus *is the collection of all points which satisfy a given condition.]*

*[Gerry Leversha, ex-St Paul's School]*

## Discussion

Let us establish notation. Let $L$ be the point of tangency of $PQ$ with the inner circle. The key to this problem is to identify something not obvious about the location of the incentre $I$ of triangle $AQP$. As usual, the only person who might not draw an accurate diagram would be that person who does not wish to solve the problem. The picture gives a big clue. Once you guess the remarkable fact about the location of $I$, then it is an interesting problem to prove that it is true. There are all sorts of dreadful (but effective) ways of doing this, by sufficiently cunning use of trigonometry or diligent application of similar triangles. However, there is also a very cute proof. If you can spot this proof, then so much the better. If not, you have to get your hands dirty. Unless you have magic powers, it seems that sometimes you will not be able to find a pretty way to prove a pretty result, especially if you are under pressure of time. In that case you need to get stuck in, and do it by brute force and ingenuity.

## Solution

See figure 16.1.

The two circles are mutually tangent at $A$. There is an enlargement with scale factor $\alpha$ from $A$ which carries the inner circle to the outer one, and carries the line $PQ$ to a parallel line which is tangent to the outer circle at $X$. Observe that the line $PQ$, the circle $AQP$ and the tangent line at $X$ are all invariant under reflection in the perpendicular bisector of the segment $PQ$, so $X$ lies on that perpendicular bisector and the two arcs $QX$ and $XP$ are reflections of one another. Therefore $X$ is the midpoint of the arc $QP$ which does not contain $A$.

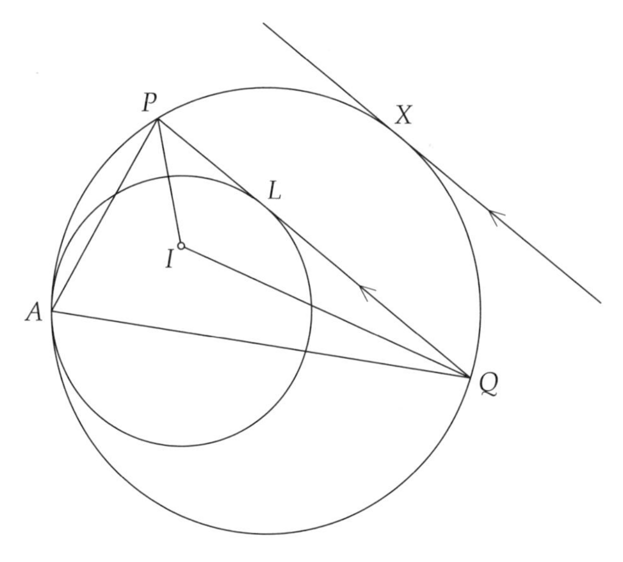


*Figure 16.1*

Equal arcs subtend equal angles, so $AX$ is the internal angle bisector at $A$, and, thanks to the enlargement, this line passes through $L$.

The incentre $I$ of triangle $AQP$ lies on $AL$, so it suffices to show that $\frac{LI}{IA}$ is constant, for then as $L$ traces out the inner circle, $I$ will also trace out a circle. Let the inner circle cross $AP$ again at $S$, The tangent-secant theorem applies, so $PL^2 = AP \times SP$. Therefore

$$\left(\frac{PL}{AP}\right)^2 = \frac{SP}{AP} = \frac{AP - AS}{AP} = 1 - \alpha.$$

The angle bisector theorem applied to triangle $LPA$ tells us that $\frac{PL}{AP} = \frac{IL}{AI}$ and so

$$\left(\frac{IL}{AI}\right)^2 = 1 - \alpha$$

and therefore $\frac{IL}{AI}$ is independent of the position of $L$ on the inner circle, and the result is proved.

There is the very picky matter of what happens if $L$ is at $A$, a degenerate situation. You might argue that this point is missing from the locus of $I$, but the markers decided to ignore this delicate distraction.

## Afterword

The idea of locating $I$ on $AL$, and then calculating the ratio $\frac{IL}{AI}$ is very natural, but there are many ways to establish that this ratio is constant. The tangent-secant theorem was used in our solution because it gives a very clean argument. However, alternative methods exist, including trigonometric calculations.

# Problem 4

Given two points $P$ and $Q$ with integer coordinates, we say that $P$ *sees* $Q$ if the line segment $PQ$ contains no other points with integer coordinates. An *n-loop* is a sequence of $n$ points $P_1$, $P_2$, ..., $P_n$, each with integer coordinates, such that the following conditions hold:

(i) $P_j$ sees $P_{j+1}$ for $1 \leq j \leq n-1$, and $P_n$ sees $P_1$;

(ii) No $P_j$ sees any $P_k$ apart from those mentioned in (a);

(iii) No three of the points lie on the same straight line.

Does there exist a 100-loop?

*[Dominic Rowland, St Paul's School]*

## Discussion

If there is no 100-loop, we will have to prove it. If there is one, then we will almost certainly have to build one. It is possible that there is a non-constructive proof of the existence of 100-loops, but that seems unlikely. If we try to build a 100-loop and fail, that may well give us a clue as to why it is impossible (if it is impossible). See figure 16.2.

Leaving aside the visibility and invisibility conditions, these 100 points need to have the property that no three of them are collinear. How can we achieve this? There are two common techniques. Either (A) choose the points one at a time, avoiding collinearity as we go or (B) pop all the points on a conic: a circle, a parabola, an ellipse or a hyperbola. Then no three can be collinear. Think hard about the problem, and decide which strategy, (A) or (B), is likely to give you better control as you attempt the construction.

## Solution

There is a 100-loop, and we will build one. The principal tool that we will use is the Chinese remainder theorem. See section 2.7 on page 30.

The points $(a, b)$ and $(c, d)$ with integral coordinates are mutually visible if, and only if, $(c-a, d-b)$ are coprime. Notice that if $(a, b)$ can (or cannot) see $(c, d)$, then the same visibility status will hold for any pair of points $(a, b+k(c-a))$ and $(c, d)$ where $k$ is an integer. This is because

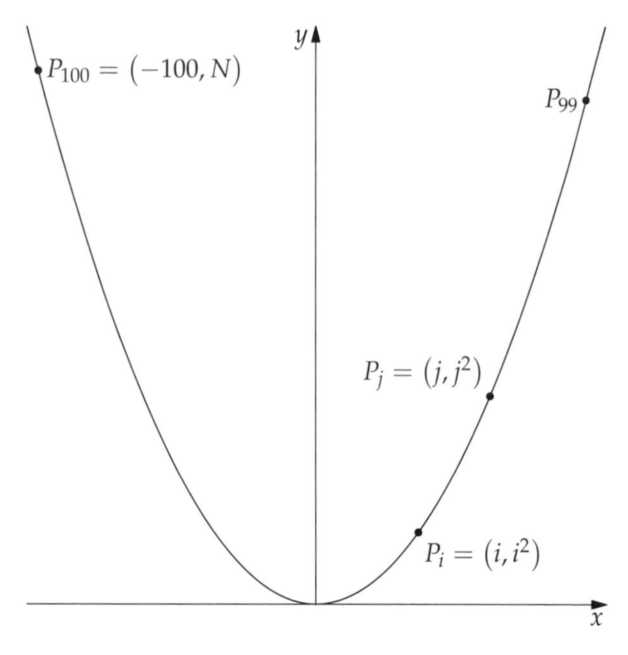


*Figure 16.2*

$c - a$ and $d - b$ are coprime if, and only if, $c - a$ and $d - b - k(c - a)$ are coprime.

We will give a solution where 99 of the points lie on the parabola $y = x^2$ in the $x, y$-coordinate plane. That will prevent unwanted collinearities among these points. The points $P_1, P_2, \ldots, P_{99}$ are $(j, j^2)$ where $j$ ranges from 1 to 99. Points with adjacent subscripts are mutually visible because the $x$-coordinates differ by 1. Otherwise if $i < j$ are different and non-adjacent subscripts, then the line joining them has slope $\dfrac{j^2 - i^2}{j - i} = i + j$, an integer. The point $(i + 1, i^2 + i + j)$ obstructs the view between $P_i$ and $P_j$.

Now we seek a point $P = (-100, N) = P_{100}$ which is visible from $P_1 = (1, 1)$ and $P_{99} = (99, 99^2)$ but from no other $P_i$, and of course $P$ needs to be chosen to avoid collinearities. Consider the point $(-100, 0)$. This is visible from $(1, 1)$ because the $y$ coordinates differ by 1, but also because 101 and 1 are coprime. Therefore 101 and $1 + 101k$ are coprime for all integers $k$ and so the points $(-100, 101k)$ all see $P_1$.

Therefore we can arrange that $P$ and $P_1$ are mutually visible by choosing the integer $N$ to satisfy the congruence

$$N \equiv 0 \pmod{101}. \tag{16.2}$$

Consider the points $(-100, 100^2)$ and $P_j$ for $1 \leq j \leq 98$. Now $j + 100$ and $j^2 - 100^2$ are not coprime, and so $(-100, 100^2)$ is invisible from these points $P_j$, as is $(-100, 100^2 + kC)$ where $C$ is the lowest common multiple (or just the product) of $102, 103, \ldots, 198$ and $k$ is any integer. We can arrange that $P$ cannot be seen be $P_j$ for $2 \leq j \leq 98$ by choosing and integer $N$ such that

$$N \equiv 100^2 \pmod{C}. \tag{16.3}$$

We now worry about finding points with $x$-coordinate $-100$ from which $P_{99}$ can be seen. The point $(-100, 99^2 - 1)$ is visible from $P_{99} = (99, 99^2)$ because 199 and 1 are coprime. Therefore, for all integers $k$, the point $(-100, 199k + 99^2 - 1)$ can see $P_{99}$. We therefore choose an integer $N$ such that

$$N \equiv 99^2 - 1 \pmod{199}. \tag{16.4}$$

Next we can deploy the Chinese remainder theorem (see section 2.7) because 101 and 199 are different primes, and neither of them divides $C$. We choose a simultaneous solution $N$ to the system of three congruences (16.2), (16.3) and (16.4). Then $P = P_{100} = (-100, N)$ has the correct visibility properties.

There remains the danger that this choice of $P_{100}$ is on some line $P_iP_j$ where $1 \leq i < j \leq 99$. There is an arithmetic progression of integers $N$ which satisfy our three congruences, so we can choose $N$ to be sufficiently large that $P_{100}$ lies above the parabola which is the graph of $y = x^2$. When $1 \leq i < j \leq 99$, the parts of the lines $P_iP_j$ on or above the parabola are finite line segments on the opposite side of the axis of symmetry of the parabola from this choice of $P_{100}$, so collinearities are avoided.

## Afterword

It is helpful to be a fluent user of Chinese remainder theorem arguments. You can prove many remarkable things about the integers using this result. Please prove that the following statements are correct.

> There are a billion consecutive positive integers each of which is divisible by a billion different prime numbers.

> There are a billion consecutive positive integers each of which is divisible by the billionth power of a prime number.

If you find these results surprising, this is perhaps because of the unhealthy human preoccupation with small positive integers (those less than $10^{10^{10}}$ for example). Try to get out more. Travel along the number line broadens the mind.

# 2016 solutions

## Problem 1

Circles of radius $r_1$, $r_2$ and $r_3$ touch each other externally, and they touch a common tangent at points $A$, $B$ and $C$ respectively, where $B$ lies between $A$ and $C$.
Prove that $16(r_1 + r_2 + r_3) \geq 9(AB + BC + CA)$.

*[Dominic Yeo, Worcester College, Oxford]*

### Discussion

The inequality to be proved is independent of scaling. If it holds for a particular configuration, then it will hold for a similar diagram where all point to point distances are multiplied by the same factor. We are therefore at liberty to assume that the distance $AC$ is 1729, or indeed anything we like. Another way to say this is that you can choose your own units of measurement.

When will equality be achieved? This is almost always an excellent question to ask when addressing an inequality problem. Even if you are not sure of the answer, an intelligent guess can be very helpful in finding a good approach. In this case we can regard scaled diagrams as being essentially the same. If there is just one configuration where equality is achieved, then by symmetry it will have to be when $r_1 = r_3$.

The most direct method is to fix $A$ and $C$, and consider a variable point $B$ between them, perhaps by means of a parameter. It would be wise to use the midpoint of $AC$ as an origin because, if our hunch is correct, then this will make the mathematics develop smoothly as it does in solution 1.

In a mathematics competition, I would expect almost all successful solvers to use solution 1, or a variation on it. However, without the pressure of time, it is an interesting and instructive amusement to see if a more geometrical method is possible. In fact it is, and we present such an approach in solution 2.

## Solution 1

Let $AB = c$, $BC = a$ and $CA = b$ (borrowing notation from a degenerate triangle). In figure 17.1 we can use the theorem of Pythagoras to see that $(r_1 + r_2)^2 = (r_1 - r_2)^2 + c^2$ and so $c = 2\sqrt{r_1 r_2}$.

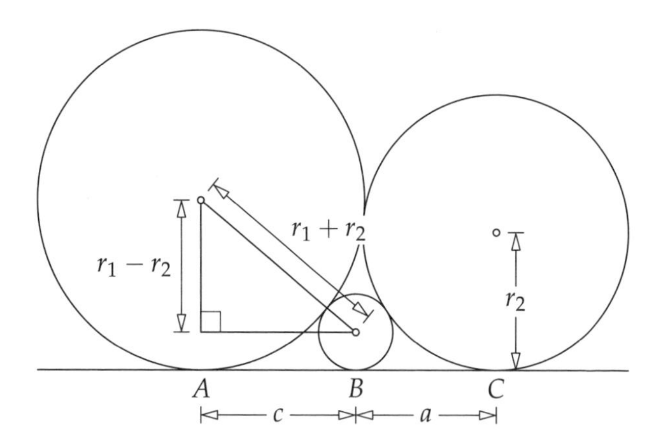


*Figure 17.1*

Similarly $a = 2\sqrt{r_2 r_3}$ and $b = 2\sqrt{r_3 r_1}$. Therefore

$$2r_1 = \frac{bc}{a}, \quad 2r_2 = \frac{ca}{b} \text{ and } 2r_3 = \frac{ab}{c}.$$

Let $b = a + c = 2$, because then we expect equality to be achieved when $a = c = 1$, and that should make the algebra attractive. Now $9(AB + BC + CA) = 9(a + b + c) = 36$. We need to show that $2r_1 + 2r_2 + 2r_3 \geq \frac{9}{2}$. We have

$$2r_1 + 2r_2 + 2r_3 = \frac{2c}{a} + \frac{ca}{2} + \frac{2a}{c} = \frac{4c^2 + c^2a^2 + 4a^2}{2ca}.$$

Let $a = 1 + x$ (with $0 \leq x < 1$) and so $c = 1 - x$, for then we expect equality when $x = 0$. Once again we set this up with an eye on keeping the algebra simple. We have

$$\begin{aligned} 2r_1 + 2r_2 + 2r_3 &= \frac{4(1-x)^2 + (1-x^2)^2 + 4(1+x)^2}{2(1-x^2)} \\ &\geq \frac{9 + 6x^2 + x^4}{2(1-x^2)} \\ &\geq \tfrac{9}{2} \end{aligned}$$

as required. The critical value of $x$ is 0, which corresponds to $r_1 = r_3$ as expected.

## Solution 2

We begin by repeating the observation made at the start of solution 1 that

$$2r_1 = \frac{bc}{a}, \quad 2r_2 = \frac{ca}{b} \text{ and } 2r_3 = \frac{ab}{c}.$$

where $AB = c$, $BC = a$ and $CA = b$. Therefore $abc = 8r_1r_2r_3$. See figure 17.2.

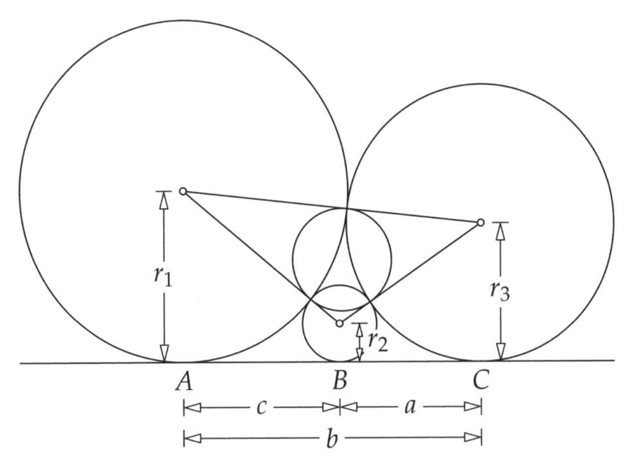


*Figure 17.2*

Let the triangle formed by the centres of the three circles have area $\triangle$ and inradius $r$. The semiperimeter $s$ of this triangle is $r_1 + r_2 + r_3$. Its vertex to incircle contact point distances are $r_1, r_2$ and $r_3$ because these distances are each the semiperimeter minus a side, and in our case that yields $r_i$ for $i = 1, 2, 3$. Heron's formula gives $\triangle^2 = sr_1r_2r_3$ so

$$8\triangle^2 = sabc \text{ and therefore } 8sr\triangle = sabc.$$

It follows that

$$\frac{1}{r} = \frac{8\triangle}{abc}. \tag{17.1}$$

We can express $\triangle$ in terms of the area of the three trapezia obtained by dropping perpendiculars from the circle centres to the common tangent. Then

$$\triangle = \tfrac{1}{2}((r_1 + r_3)b - (r_1 + r_2)c - (r_2 + r_3)a).$$

When the smoke clears we find that

$$\triangle = \tfrac{1}{2}(r_1a + r_3c - r_2b) = \tfrac{1}{4}(ab + bc - ca). \tag{17.2}$$

The AM-GM inequality (page 14) gives $ac \leq \dfrac{b^2}{4}$ and so

$$\frac{1}{ac} \geq \frac{4}{b^2} \tag{17.3}$$

$$\text{and} \quad -ac \geq -\frac{b^2}{4}. \tag{17.4}$$

Now use equations (17.1) and (17.2) to discover that

$$\frac{1}{r} = \frac{2}{abc}(ab + bc - ac) = 2\left(\frac{1}{a} + \frac{1}{c} - \frac{1}{b}\right)$$

and then deploy (17.3) to learn that

$$\frac{1}{r} = 2\left(\frac{b}{ac} - \frac{1}{b}\right) \geq 2\left(\frac{4}{b} - \frac{1}{b}\right) = \frac{6}{b}.$$

Now

$$s = \frac{abc}{8r^2} = \frac{1}{r}\left(\frac{abc}{4}\left(\frac{b}{ac} - \frac{1}{b}\right)\right)$$

and (17.4) comes into play and gives

$$s \geq \frac{6}{b} \times \frac{1}{4}(b^2 - ac) \geq \frac{3}{2b}\left(\frac{3b^2}{4}\right) \geq \frac{9b}{8}.$$

Therefore

$$16(r_1 + r_2 + r_3) = 16s \geq 18b = 9(AB + BC + CA).$$

## Afterword

René Descartes proved the four circles theorem. This formula relates the radii of four circle in the plane where each one is tangent to the other three. If the radii are $r_1$, $r_2$, $r_3$ and $r_4$ and the four circles touch externally then

$$\left(\frac{1}{r_1^2}+\frac{1}{r_2^2}+\frac{1}{r_3^2}+\frac{1}{r_4^2}\right)=\frac{1}{2}\left(\frac{1}{r_1}+\frac{1}{r_2}+\frac{1}{r_3}+\frac{1}{r_4}\right)^2.$$

The theorem applies to our configuration, where the straight line is regarded as a circle of infinite radius, and we deem the reciprocal of infinity to be 0. The reader should verify this. You change the sign of $\frac{1}{r_i}$ if the corresponding circle touches another internally.

This theorem was rediscovered by Frederick Soddy. He summarized the result in a piece of doggerel, *The Kiss Precise*, which can be found on the internet.

# Problem 2

Alison has compiled a list of 20 hockey teams, ordered by how good she thinks they are, but refuses to share it. Benjamin may mention three teams to her, and she will then choose either to tell him which she thinks is the weakest team of the three, or which she thinks is the strongest team of the three. Benjamin may do this as many times as he likes.

Determine the largest $N$ such that Benjamin can guarantee to be able to find a sequence $T_1, T_2, \ldots, T_N$ of teams with the property that he knows that Alison thinks that $T_i$ is better than $T_{i+1}$ for each $1 \leq i < N$.

*[James Cranch, University of Sheffield]*

## Discussion

Benjamin may mention the same three teams more than once, but he has no guarantee that Alison might choose to give a different response. Therefore we can assume that Benjamin only mentions a particular group of three teams once. Also, it is in Benjamin's interest to gather as much information as possible, so he may as well ask about all $\binom{20}{3} = 1140$ possibilities. If Alison tossed a coin to decide whether to reveal the top team or the bottom team on each occasion, then Benjamin would have a vast amount of useful information, and could almost certainly construct Alison's ranking. However, if Alison employs a clever strategy to choose which answers to give in order to restrict the information which Benjamin obtains, then Benjamin will have difficulty in determining Alison's ranking. Since we are looking for the largest possible value of $N$ teams that Benjamin can guarantee to rank correctly, we may assume that Alison is employing a strategy to make Benjamin's life difficult.

Note, by the way, that $N \geq 2$, since after mentioning just one group of three teams, and hearing Alison's response, Benjamin will be able correctly to supply two lists of two teams in the correct ranking. Suppose that Benjamin asks about $A, B$ and $C$ and in fact Alison thinks that $A$ is better than $B$, and that $B$ is better than $C$. Write this as $A > B$ and $B > C$. If Alison answers that $A$ is the strongest of the these three teams, Benjamin then knows $A > B$ and $A > C$. On the other hand, if Alison answers that $C$ is the weakest of these three teams, then Benjamin knows that $A > C$ and $B > C$.

## Solution

Alison ranks the team $A_1 > A_2 > \cdots > A_{20}$. Alison can hide her judgement of the relative merits of $A_1$ and $A_2$. Whenever she is asked about three teams $A_1, A_2$ and $A_i$, then she can answer that $A_i$ is the weakest. Her answers would be exactly the same if $A_1$ and $A_2$ swapped rank position, so there is no way for Benjamin to work out which team has the top rank.

In fact Alison can hide other things too. Whenever she is asked about teams $A_{2n-1}, A_{2n}$ and $A_j$, then $A_j$ is ranked higher or lower than the consecutive pair, and she can elect to mention that $A_j$ is strongest, or weakest, depending on which is true. She answers honestly and arbitrarily to all other questions. All answers that she gives are consistent with swapping the rank order of $A_{2n-1}$ and $A_{2n}$ for every $n$.

Whenever Benjamin asks about three teams which have consecutive rankings $A_iA_{i+1}A_{i+2}$, then Alison's response enables him to deduce that $A_i > A_{i+2}$ for $i = 1, 2, \ldots, 18$. After the verbal exchanges are completed, Benjamin can deduce that $T_1 > T_2 > \cdots > T_{10}$ in two cases: when $T_i = A_{2i-1}$ for all $i$ and when $T_i = A_{2i}$ for all $i$. Therefore $N \geq 10$.

Next we show that $N < 11$. Suppose, for contradiction, that Benjamin can deduce the correct ordering of 11 teams. Now apply a Dirichlet principle (pigeon-hole) argument. The 10 pigeon-holes are the sets $\{1,2\}, \{3,4\}, \ldots \{19,20\}$. Any collection of 11 different numbers in the range 1 to 20 (inclusive) will have two members in the same pigeon-hole. However, Benjamin cannot determine the relative rankings of teams $A_{2n-1}, A_{2n}$ for any $n$. Therefore Benjamin cannot determine Alison's rankings of any collection of 11 teams and so $N < 11$. Therefore $N = 10$.

## Afterword

Another way of thinking about this problem is to suppose that Alison has written down her ranking, and is suffering from partial amnesia. For each $i$ she can remember which teams were in position $2i - 1$ and $2i$, but has forgotten which is which. She can avoid having to consult her written list by using the strategy outlined in the solution. She cannot disclose information which she cannot remember.

You can show that the information hidden by Alison's answers is the only information that Benjamin cannot learn. Benjamin can determine which teams are ranked first and second, and also which teams are ranked third and fourth and so on. Benjamin can therefore give $2^{10} = 1024$ lists of 10 correctly ranked teams, and they come in 512 complementary pairs (with no teams in common). Benjamin cannot determine which of these 512 pairs is the one consisting of the even ranked and odd ranked teams.

To see this concretely, suppose that there are only four teams, and Alison ranks them $A > B > C > D$. Benjamin asks about $A, B$ and $C$ and learns that $A > C$ and $B > C$. Benjamin asks about $A, B$ and $D$ and learns that $A > D$ and $B > D$. Benjamin asks about $A, C$ and $D$ and hears that $A > C$ and $A > D$ which he knew already. Finally Benjamin asks about $B, C$ and $D$ and hears that $B > C$ and $B > D$ which, again, he knew already. There are four possible rankings which are consistent with the answers Benjamin has heard: $A > B > C > D$, $B > A > C > D$, $A > B > D > C$ and $B > A > D > C$. Benjamin is not in a position to identify which is correct.

Now return to the 20 team game. Think about what would happen if you changed the parameters of the game. Suppose that Alison had a third option, and could mention a team and say that it was the middle ranking of the three teams. How would things change? Another variation is to let Benjamin mention four teams rather than three, and Alison be allowed to mention which is the strongest or the weakest of the four. What would happen?

# Problem 3

Let $ABCD$ be a cyclic quadrilateral. The diagonals $AC$ and $BD$ meet at $P$, and $DA$ and $CB$ produced meet at $Q$. The midpoint of $AB$ is $E$.

Prove that if $PQ$ is perpendicular to $AC$, then $PE$ is perpendicular to $BC$.

*[David Monk, ex-University of Edinburgh]*

## Discussion

The first difficulty with this problem is to work out how to draw the diagram. This can be done by drawing an acute triangle $AQC$. Let $P$ on the line segment $AC$ be the foot of the perpendicular from $Q$. Select $B$ on $QC$ such that $\angle QBP = \angle CAQ$ and let the line $BP$ meet the line $QA$ at $D$. Arranging that $\angle QBP$ and $\angle CAQ$ are approximately the same is possible by eye, and yields the plausible figure 17.3. You might work out how to do this precisely using a straight edge and compasses construction.

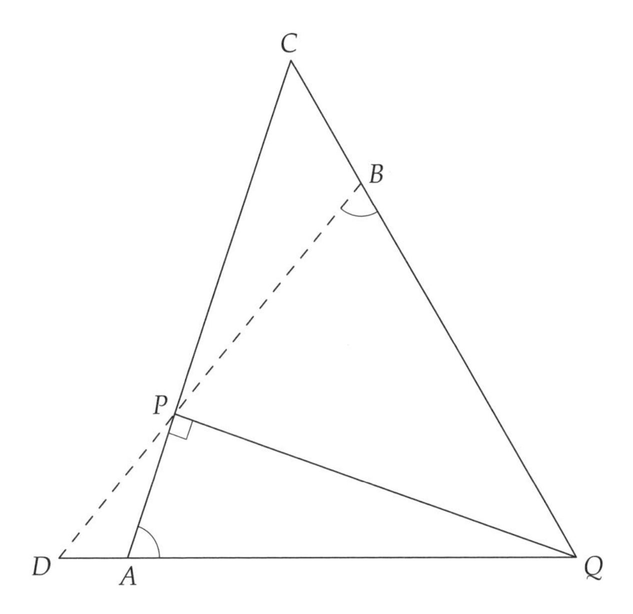


*Figure 17.3*

By taking supplements, $\angle DBC = \angle DAC$ and so $ABCD$ is a cyclic quadrilateral. This quadrilateral is clockwise or anticlockwise depending on the relative sizes of $\angle CAQ$ and $\angle QCA$.

We have to work out how to exploit the condition that $E$ is the midpoint of $AB$.

## Solution 1

Choose $A'$ on the line $AC$ so that $P$ is the midpoint of $AA'$, as illustrated in figure 17.4.

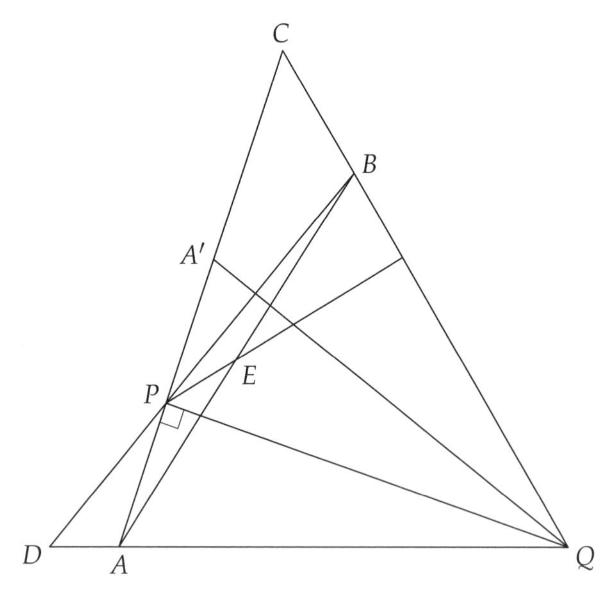


*Figure 17.4*

Now $\angle QA'P = \angle PAQ$, by reflection in $PQ$. However $\angle PAQ = \angle QBP$ since the supplements of these two angles are $\angle DAC$ and $\angle DBC$, which are equal angles in the same segment of the circle $ABCD$. Therefore $\angle QA'P = \angle QBP$. By the converse of angles in the same segment, the quadrilateral $QBA'P$ is cyclic. Opposite angles of the cyclic quadrilateral $QBA'P$ are supplementary so $A'B$ is perpendicular to the line $BC$. The segment $PE$ is the enlargement of the segment $A'B$ from $A$ with scale factor $\frac{1}{2}$, so $PE$ is parallel to $A'B$, and therefore $PE$ is perpendicular to $BC$.

## Solution 2

The circle with centre $E$ has $AB$ as a diameter. Let this circle cross $CB$ produced again at $F$. By the angle in a semicircle theorem (Thales), $AF$ is perpendicular to $CB$. By the converse of the same theorem, the points $AQFP$ are concyclic so $\angle DAP = \angle QFP$. Now $\angle DAP = \angle DAC = \angle DBC = \angle PBC$ by angles in the same segment. Therefore $\angle QFP = \angle PBC$. Taking supplements of these angles, we discover that $\angle PFB = \angle FBP$. Therefore triangle $BPF$ is isosceles with apex $P$ and so $PB = PF$. The altitude through $P$ of this isosceles triangle meets $BC$ produced at $Z$, so $PZ$ is perpendicular to the line $BF$ which is the line $BC$, and so $PZ$ is parallel to $AF$. See figure 17.5.

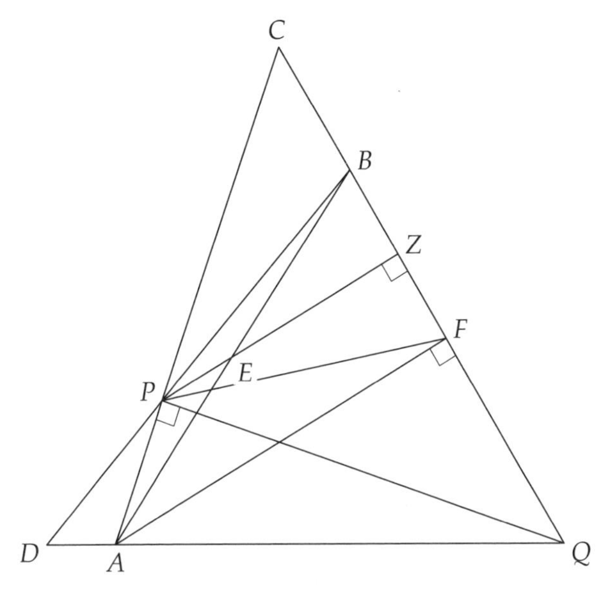


Figure 17.5

Now $BZ = ZF$, so the line $AF$ is the result of enlarging the line $PZ$ from $B$ with scale factor 2, but this enlargement carries $E$ to $A$. Therefore $E$ is on $PZ$ and so the lines $PZ$ and $PE$ are the same. Therefore $PE$ is perpendicular to $BC$.

## Some unproved theoretical background

Next we present a more sophisticated solution which relies on the theory of the polar line of a point $Q$ with respect to a circle.

If you draw any pair of straight lines through a point $Q$, the first meeting the circle at $U$ and $V$, and the second meeting the circle at $X$ and $Y$, then as these two lines vary, the locus of all points $Z$ such that $Z$ is the intersection of $UY$ and $VX$ is a line (the *polar line* of $Q$). If $Q$ happens to lie outside the circle, you can choose lines through $Q$ to be the tangent lines from $Q$ to the circle, and it follows that this polar line passes through the contact points of the circle with the tangent lines through $Q$. See figure 17.6. It follows that $UX$ and $VY$ also meet on the polar line.

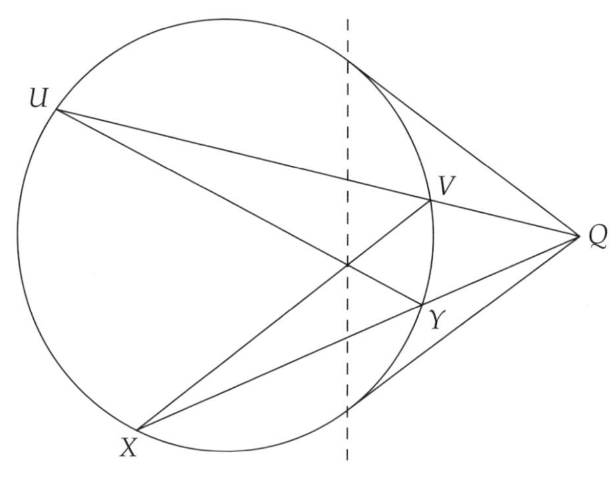


*Figure 17.6*

If $Q$ is on the circle, its polar line is the tangent line at $Q$. It is possible that $Q$ lies inside the circle of course, and the reader is invited to draw diagrams and see the polar line emerge.

In vector terms, if the circle has centre $O$ and radius $R$, then the polar line of $Q$ is the locus of all points $P$ such that $\boldsymbol{OP}.\boldsymbol{OQ} = R^2$. The reader who is interested in polar lines, and the beautiful associated theory of projective duality, should research this topic, perhaps in Gerry Leversha's *Geometry of the Triangle*, UKMT. Notice the symmetry of the expression $\boldsymbol{OP}.\boldsymbol{OQ} = R^2$, which yields the fact that $P$ is on the polar line of $Q$ if, and only if, $Q$ is on the polar line of $P$.

## Solution 3

Let the circle $ABCD$ have centre $O$ and radius $R$. We seek to show that $(\boldsymbol{PA}+\boldsymbol{PB}).\boldsymbol{QC}=0$.

Now

$$\begin{aligned}(\boldsymbol{PA}+\boldsymbol{PB}).\boldsymbol{QC} &= \boldsymbol{PA}.(\boldsymbol{QP}+\boldsymbol{PC})+\boldsymbol{PB}.\boldsymbol{QC}\\ &= \boldsymbol{PA}.\boldsymbol{PC}+(\boldsymbol{PQ}+\boldsymbol{QB}).\boldsymbol{QC}\\ &= OP^2-R^2-PQ^2+\boldsymbol{QB}.\boldsymbol{QC}\\ &= OP^2-R^2-PQ^2+OQ^2-R^2.\end{aligned}$$

but by the cosine rule, $OP^2+OQ^2-PQ^2 = 2\boldsymbol{OP}.\boldsymbol{OQ}$. Therefore the condition that $(\boldsymbol{PA}+\boldsymbol{PB}).\boldsymbol{QC}=0$ is equivalent to the condition that $\boldsymbol{OP}.\boldsymbol{OQ}=R^2$. Geometrically this is the condition that $P$ is on the polar line of $Q$, and it is.

## Afterword

First consider synthetic Euclidean approaches similar to solution 1. Identifying the importance of $F$ is the key to this solution, and it does not matter if you introduce it using the circle on diameter $AQ$, or by dropping the perpendicular from $A$.

For solution 2, it helps a lot if you realize that the powers of $P$ and $Q$ are likely to be in the game. This encourages you to work with vectors which begin at $P$ and $Q$ and point elsewhere, since that gives you access to $\boldsymbol{PA}.\boldsymbol{PC}=OP^2-R^2$ and $\boldsymbol{QB}.\boldsymbol{QC}=OQ^2-R^2$. Wanting to get at these expressions imposes a sense of purpose which makes the algebra straightforward. We started with the condition $(\boldsymbol{PA}+\boldsymbol{PB}).\boldsymbol{QC}=0$. It would have been mathematically correct, but unhelpful, to start with the equivalent condition $(\boldsymbol{PA}+\boldsymbol{PB}).\boldsymbol{BC}$. It is always possible to write a vector as the sum of two others, but if you do that randomly, you are unlikely to discover anything of interest.

# Problem 4

Suppose that $p$ is a prime number and that there are different positive integers $u$ and $v$ such that $p^2$ is the mean of $u^2$ and $v^2$.

Prove that $2p - u - v$ is a square or twice a square.

*[Geoff Smith, University of Bath]*

## Discussion

We give three solutions below, the first of which is extremely short. However, this does not mean that it is easy to find unless you have some experience solving olympiad level number theory problems. The other solutions do not involve having the insight to bring $2p + u + v$ into the fray.

## Solution 1

We may assume that $p$ is odd since 4 is not the mean of different squares. Now $u$ and $v$ are different and so neither is $p$. However, $u^2 + v^2 = 2p^2$ so $0 < u, v < 2p$ so $uv$ is not divisible by $p$. Therefore $(u + v)^2 = 2p^2 - 2uv$ is not divisible by $p$.

Consider $(2p - u - v)(2p + u + v) = 4p^2 - u^2 - v^2 - 2uv = (u - v)^2$ which is a non-zero square, so $2p - u - v$ is positive. Any odd common factor of $2p - u - v$ and $2p + u + v$ divides $p$ and $u + v$ t is always possible to write a vector as the sum of two others, but if you do that randomly, you are unlikely to discover anything of interest. It is always possible to write a vector as the sum of two others, but if you do that randomly, you are unlikely to discover anything of interest. and so be 1. Therefore each of $2p - u - v$ and $2p + u + v$ is a square or twice a square.

## Solution 2

We may assume that $u < p < v$. Define positive integers $a$ and $b$ by $p - b = u$ and $p + a = v$ so $2p - u - v = b - a$. The average condition is that

$$(p - b)^2 + (p + a)^2 = 2p^2,$$

which is equivalent to $2pa + a^2 = 2pb - b^2$. Therefore $2p(b - a) = a^2 + b^2 = (b - a)^2 + 2ab$. Let $m = b - a > 0$ so $m$ divides $2ab$. If $m$ were odd, then $\dfrac{2ab}{m}$ would be even, and this contradicts

$$2p = m + \frac{2ab}{m}.$$

Therefore $m$ is even.

Observe that 4 is not the average of two different squares so $p$ is odd. Choose any $q$ an odd prime divisor of $m$. If $p = q$, then $m \geq 2p$ and so $\dfrac{2ab}{m} \leq 0$. This is impossible because $a$ and $b$ are positive integers. Therefore $q \neq p$.

Now

$$m + \frac{2ab}{m} = m + \frac{2a(a+m)}{m} = m + 2a + \frac{2a^2}{m}$$

and so $\dfrac{2a^2}{m}$ is an integer. Therefore the odd prime number $q$ divides $a^2$ and so divides $a$. The integer $\dfrac{2a^2}{m}$ is not divisible by $q$, else $q$ would divide $2p$ which it does not. It follows that the power of $q$ which divides $m$ is the same as the power of $q$ which divides $a^2$, so this power is even. This remark applies to all odd primes dividing $m$, and the proof is complete.

## Solution 3

Notice that $2^2$ is not the average of different positive squares, so every prime $p$ satisfying the conditions of the problem is odd. We may assume that $u < p < v$ and so $p - u < p + u < p + v$. Now $p^2$ is the mean of $u^2$ and $v^2$ so that $(p-u)(p+u) = (v-p)(v+p)$. Our chain of two inequalities may therefore be extended to a chain of three inequalities:

$$v - p < p - u < p + u < v + p.$$

The first of these inequalities rearranges to reveal $u + v < 2p$. Also $(u+v)^2 - 2uv = 2p^2$ so $(u+v)^2 > 2p^2 > p^2$ and therefore $u + v > p$. Thus we have trapped $u + v$ in the range $p < u + v < 2p$. It follows that $u + v$ is coprime with the prime number $p$.

Write

$$\frac{p-u}{v-p} = \frac{b}{a} = \frac{v+p}{p+u}$$

with integers $0 < a < b$ in lowest terms. We cross multiply to obtain a pair of linear equations in $u$ and $v$:

$$ap - au = bv - bp;$$
$$bp + bu = av + ap.$$

Eliminating one of $u$ and $v$ at a time we obtain $u(a^2+b^2) = (a^2+2ab-b^2)p$ and $v(a^2+b^2) = (b^2+2ab-a^2)p$. Add to get $(u+v)(a^2+b^2) = 4abp$. Notice that $a$ and $b$ are coprime to $a^2+b^2$ so $ab \mid u+v$. Also we established that $p$ does not divide $u+v$ so $p$ divides $u+v$. If $a$ and $b$ are both odd then $a^2+b^2 = 2 \pmod 4$, so $u+v = 2ab$, $a^2+b^2 = 2p$ and $2p-u-v = (b-a)^2$. If one of $a$ and $b$ is even then $a^2+b^2 = 1 \pmod 4$, so $u+v = 4ab$, $a^2+b^2 = p$ and $2p-u-v = (b-a)^2$. Notice that it also follows that $2p+u+v = (a+b)^2$ in both cases.

## Afterword

You might wonder if there are any prime numbers with squares which are the average of different squares. Here is one: $5^2 = \frac{1}{2}(1^2+7^2)$ and indeed $10-1-7 = 2 \times 1^1$ and $10+1+7 = 18 = 2 \times 3^2$. Are there any more examples? Are there infinitely many examples?

# Fictional IMO solutions

## Background

The film $X + Y$ was made in several locations. An International Mathematical Olympiad forms part of the story, and the film set for the actual exam was Sheffield Town Hall. The filming took place at a week-end, so that municipal governance would be uninterrupted.

I had been invited to attend the filming as an observer. The film production team had secured permission from UKMT and the IMO to use their emblems and flags, and various people connected with the British and International Mathematical Olympiads were in the film as extras. The person on the film set responsible for keeping the mathematics correct was Lee Zhou Zhao. In real life he was a member of the UK team at IMO 2006 in Slovenia, and he had a non-speaking role in the film as a member of the UK team. His punting skills were put to good use in scenes filmed on the river Cam. The other UK IMO person who features heavily in the film is Joseph Myers. He is often on screen, but again does not speak.

At very short notice, I received a message from the production team that they wanted mathematical olympiad style problems for an exam paper to be on the desks during the exam. There was no time to do anything clever, so I simply withdrew some problems which I had already submitted for possible use in the British Mathematical Olympiad, and created a paper in a few minutes. The reason that they wanted a real exam paper was to entertain the many young mathematicians who were extras in the exam hall.

The director, Morgan Matthews, decided to vary the wording of Problem 1 in the film, in order to introduce colours and trains into the mind of the lead character. While mathematically irrelevant, this gave another opportunity to emphasize the synaesthesia which accompanied the thought processes of the character Nathan Ellis. This tinkering was done retrospectively, and the exam questions that were actually sitting on the desks in the film were the ones here.

# Problem 1

A $2n \times 2n$ board is divided into $4n^2$ small squares in the manner of a chessboard. Each small square is painted with one of four colours so that every $2 \times 2$ block of four small squares involves all four colours. Prove that the four corner squares of the board are painted with different colours.

*[Geoff Smith, University of Bath]*

## Discussion

This is a straightforward problem, and really belongs on a BMO1 level paper. Working out which patterns can arise is simply a matter of exploration, though finding a neat way to write it up may not be so easy.

## Solution

Distinguish between horizontal rows and vertical columns.

We say that a row or column is *alternating* if it involves just two colours, with no pair of adjacent square cells being of the same colour.

The colouring condition in the statement ensures that if any one row is alternating, then so is every other row. In such circumstances, the pairs of colours in adjacent rows is different. Now $2n$ is even, so the end squares of each row are of different colour, and the top and bottom rows involve different pairs of colours. In this case, the four corner small squares are coloured differently. Similar remarks apply if there is an alternating column.

Suppose that there is no alternating row. Therefore top row contains three differently coloured adjacent square cells. The colouring condition in the statement forces the three square cells immediately underneath to be coloured differently from one another. This argument continues, and we generate three adjacent alternating columns. Thus there is an alternating row or an alternating column.

## Afterword

This problem was far too easy to appear on a real IMO paper.

# Problem 2

Which positive integers $n$ have the property that $\{1, 2, \ldots, n\}$ can be partitioned into two subsets $A$ and $B$ so that the sum of the squares of the elements of $A$ is the sum of the squares of the elements of $B$?

*[Geoff Smith, University of Bath]*

## Discussion

It is clear how to begin; look at small values of $n$. You should be able to demonstrate that various values of $n$ render such a partition impossible. The harder part of the problem is to determine, with proof, which values of $n$ allow the partition. I am hesitant about claiming authorship of this problem, since I have had the feeling that I read it somewhere long ago. Whether that is true, or imagined, I cannot tell. Naturally if a reader can point out an earlier source, I will happily reassign responsibility for this question, and grovel appropriately, in any future edition of this book.

## Solution

Notice that $m^2 - (m-1)^2 = (m-2)^2 - (m-3)^2 + 4$ for each integer $m$, so

$$m^2 - (m-1)^2 - (m-2)^2 + (m-3)^2 - (m-4)^2 + (m-5)^2 + (m-6)^2 - (m-7)^2 = 0.$$

Therefore if the result holds for $N$, then it holds for $N+8$.

The sum of the first $n$ squares is even if, and only if, $n$ is 0 or 3 modulo 4. This is a necessary condition for the condition to hold. By inspection, the result does not hold when $n = 3, 4$. It holds when $n = 7$ by putting $m = 7$ in the displayed formula above, and discarding the irrelevant $0^2$ term. It holds when $n = 8$ by putting $m = 8$ in the displayed formula above.

When $n = 12$, the result holds because half the sum of the first 12 squares is

$$325 = 12^2 + 10^2 + 8^2 + 4^2 + 1^2.$$

The result holds when $n = 11$ because half the sum of the first 11 squares is

$$253 = 11^2 + 9^2 + 5^2 + 4^2 + 3^2 + 1^2.$$

Therefore the result holds when $n$ is at least 8 and is divisible by 4, and when $n$ is at least 7 and leaves remainder 3 on division by 4, and does not hold for any other positive integer $n$.

### Afterword

This might make a plausible IMO Problem 1, and could have appeared on a BMO2 paper.

## Problem 3

This problem concerns polynomials in $x$ with real coefficients.
Let $f(x) = 2013x + 1$. Suppose that $g(x)$ and $h(x)$ are polynomials such that $f(g(x)) = g(f(x))$ and $f(h(x)) = h(f(x))$.
Prove that $g(h(x)) = h(g(x))$.

*[Geoff Smith, University of Bath]*

### Discussion

It seems highly unlikely that the value of 2013 is significant, and it is cumbersome. Therefore it seem a good idea to replace it by a symbol, say $k$. The result looks so strange that a way forward suggests itself. Understand those polynomials $g(x)$ such that $f(g(x)) = g(f(x))$, and then the result is obvious.

Suppose that $g(x)$ has the commuting property under investigation. Notice that if $z$ is a fixed point of $f$, that is, $f(z) = z$, then $g(z) = g(f(z)) = f(g(z))$ since $g$ and $f$ commute in the manner specified. Therefore $g(z)$ is also a fixed point of $f$. Understanding the fixed points of $f$ is therefore a priority.

## Solution

Let $k = 2013$, and $c = -\dfrac{1}{2012}$ be the unique fixed point of $f$ (that is, $f(c) = c$).

First we study $g$. Now $g(c) = g(f(c)) = f(g(c))$ so $g(c) = c$. Therefore $g = (x - c)q + c$ where $q$ (or $q(x)$) is a real polynomial. Now $f(g(x)) = g(f(x))$ and we can write $f$ as $k(x - c) + c$. Therefore

$$k(x - c)q + c = k(x - c)q(f(x)) + c$$

and so $q(x) = q(f(x))$. Now $1 < f(1) = 2014$, and inductively $f^i(1) < f^{i+1}(1)$ for every positive integer $i$. It follows that $q(x) - q(1)$ has infinitely many roots and so is the zero polynomial. Thus $q(x)$ is $u$, a constant polynomial. Therefore $g = u(x - c) + c$.

Conversely if $g = u(x - c) + c$ for some constant $u$, then $f(g(x))$ is $uk(x - c) + c$ and this is also $g(f(x))$. The polynomials $g$ which composition-commute with $f$ are precisely the polynomials of degree at most 1 such that $g(c) = c$.

Now suppose that $g$ is $u(x - c) + c$ and $h = v(x - c) + c$ are any two such polynomials, then $g(h(x)) = uv(x - c) + c = h(g(x))$ as required.

## Afterword

The unique fixed point $c$ of $f$ plays such an important role in this problem that it worth shifting the origin so that the new origin is at $(c, 0)$. This is exactly what we did when we wrote polynomials not as polynomials in $x$, but as polynomials in the quantity $x - c$. To find the constant term of an ordinary polynomial in $x$, you evaluate it at 0, but to find the constant term of the same polynomial rearranged to be a polynomial in $x - c$, you evaluate it at $c$.

This story has a moral, of wide applicability in mathematics and indeed in life. If it does not matter where you stand, then stand in a place which makes things as simple as possible. For example, if you are going to use vectors to do some triangle geometry, and you have a choice of the origin, then use your freedom wisely. Mostly the best place for the origin is at the circumcentre of the triangle, but there are times when it is more happily placed at the centroid of the triangle, or somewhere even more peculiar. An example from algebra is the process of *completing the square* which is at the heart of understanding quadratic polynomials. If you are studying the roots of $ax^2 + bx + c$, then the ideal choice of origin is on the axis of symmetry, the vertical line through the midpoint $\frac{-b}{2a}$ of the roots. The reward for writing our quadratic as a polynomial in $x + \frac{b}{2a}$ is that it becomes

$$a\left(x+\frac{b}{2a}\right)^2+\frac{4ac-b^2}{4a^2}$$

with roots

$$\frac{-b \pm \sqrt{b^2-4ac}}{2a}.$$

Mathematics rewards us for making the right choice of origin by handing us the roots described using their midpoint $\frac{-b}{2a}$ and the distance between them $\frac{\sqrt{b^2-4ac}}{|a|}$.

# Bibliography


[1] C. J. Bradley. *Introduction to Inequalities*. UKMT, 2010. ISBN: 978-1-906001-11-7.

[2] C. J. Bradley. *Introduction to Number Theory*. UKMT, 2010. ISBN: 978-1-906001-12-4.

[3] C. J. Bradley and A. D. Gardiner. *Plane Euclidean Geometry*. UKMT, 2005. ISBN: 978-0-95368-23-6-2.

[4] Kiran S. Kedlaya. *Geometry Unbound*. 2006. URL: `http://kskedlaya.org/geometryunbound/`.

[5] Gerry Leversha. *Crossing the Bridge*. UKMT, 2008. ISBN: 978-1-906001-06-3.

[6] Gerry Leversha. *The Geometry of the Triangle*. UKMT, 2013. ISBN: 978-1-906001-17-9.

[7] Gerry Leversha and Dominic Rowland. *Introduction to Combinatorics*. UKMT, 2015. ISBN: 978-1-906001-24-7.

[8] David Monk. *New Problems in Euclidean Geometry*. UKMT, 2009. ISBN: 978-1-906001-09-4.

[9] Geoff Smith. *A Mathematical Olympiad Primer*. UKMT, 2008. ISBN: 978-1-906001-03-2.

# Index